201

THINGS TO DO

While You're Getting Better

(AT HOME OR IN THE HOSPITAL)

*How to Successfully Cope With Boredom
and Pain Without Losing Your Sanity*

ERICA LEVY KLEIN

Foreword by John Daniels, M.D.

Library of Congress Cataloging-in-Publication Data

Klein, Erica Levy.
    201 things to do while you're getting better (at home or in the hospital) : how to successfully cope with boredom and pain without losing your sanity / written and edited by Erica Levy Klein.
        p.   cm.
    Includes bibliographical references and index.
    ISBN 1-56561-033-4 : $10.95
    1. Stress management.   2. Amusements.
    3. Sick—Recreation.
    I. Title.   II.Title: Two hundred things to do while you're getting better.
    RA785.K59   1993
    615.5'07—dc20   93-23404
                                                    CIP

Cover and Text Design: Nancy Eato
Production Coordinator: Claire Lewis
Printed in the United States

Published by:
CHRONIMED Publishing
P.O. Box 47945
Minneapolis, MN 55447-9727

For three therapists who made a difference,
Madge Treeger, Jean Chase, and David Levy

Acknowledgments

I'd like to extend my heartfelt thanks to all of the authors, publishers, organizations, cartoon syndicates, and magazines that allowed me to use the material included in this book. They are listed individually with each excerpt. My deepest gratitude also to David Wexler and Donna Hoel of CHRONIMED Publishing of Minneapolis who believed in this project right from the start and shepherded it every step of the way. And to my husband, Ken Kroll, who provided love, support, and transportation during the countless late nights and still earlier mornings that resulted in this book.

A NOTE ABOUT THE INFORMATION IN THIS BOOK

Although *201 Thing to Do While You're Getting Better* is an "information celebration" that draws from many reputable sources, it is not meant to substitute for professional advice from your health care provider. Our litigious society being what it is, if you choose to follow any of the advice in this book, you do so at your own initiative.

Also, please note that information about the availability or pricing of certain items or services may be subject to change even though the facts were carefully checked before publication.

Please write to me at the address below if you discover any of the information in this book is no longer current or if you have suggestions of your own. I always welcome your thoughts and comments.

Erica Levy Klein
c/o CHRONIMED Publishing
13911 Ridgedale Drive
Minnetonka, MN 55305

Contents

A FEW WORDS FROM A CARING FRIEND

Even in today's world of medical miracles, recuperating from an illness, accident, or surgery can be a surprisingly difficult and lonely process. Not only can progress seem maddeningly slow, but boredom and pain often remind you that you are physically vulnerable and temporarily powerless.

This book was written to lessen those unpleasant feelings, to empower you as much as possible, and to comfort you at a time in your life when you may be feeling anywhere from slightly "out of it" to completely incapacitated. Having been a hospital patient myself and having helped friends and loved ones through the same process, I have very few unrealistic expectations about what you will be able to accomplish using a paperback book as your one and only guide to faster healing.

But I still cherish the hope that *201 Thing to Do While You're Getting Better* will be able to do what a loving friend or family member would do if he or she was sitting beside you—hold your hand, distract you, amuse you, and help you cope with all the aspects of being "on the mend" in a hospital, nursing home, convalescent center, or even in your own home.

Which brings us to why this book is such a shameless hodgepodge of inspiration and information, suggestions and tips, factoids, diversions, and amusements. It's because I fully intend for it to be the first-ever adult activity book for the indisposed—a grown-up, connect-the-dots book for the over-21 set.

You'll find the information presented here in dozens of easy-to-digest small sections so you don't have to wade through lots of pages when all you want to do is make it to the next pain shot or to the next round of visiting hours. And you'll not only discover how to cope with pain and discomfort a little better but get lots of tips on proven "boredom busters"—those diversions and activities that tend to make the hours fly by when all the minutes seem to want to do is crawl.

I hope you'll find *201 Thing to Do While You're Getting Better* both helpful and hopeful. It was written by a caring friend you don't know yet—me—as I thought of your special needs during these difficult days. I wish you only good things and hope you'll write to me with your own suggestions for future editions. In the meantime, I'll simply close by saying a heartfelt prayer for your speedy recovery and your return to complete health very soon.

—Erica Levy Klein
September, 1993

FOREWORD

As a physician I am constantly reminded about how important it is for someone ill or injured to experience what I call a "quality recuperation." In the many cases I've observed, the positive nature of the recuperation and the degree to which the patient felt in control of his or her situation played a key role in their steady progress and their return to good health.

Even when patients were dealing with chronic pain or a terminal illness, the way they spent their hours in the hospital or at home made a tremendous difference in how they lived their lives and how they related to others.

Whenever I think of how much a quality recuperation can mean to someone, I remember Sarah, a 56-year-old woman admitted to the hospital with a heart attack complicated by pneumonia. After bypass surgery and 6 weeks of intensive high-tech medical care, I was finally able to send Sarah home with an excellent prognosis. Naturally, I thought she'd be delighted, but as an attendant wheeled her to her son's waiting car, she seemed overwhelmingly sad. I asked her what was wrong and she told me, "I feel like I've been here for 6 years instead of 6 weeks. Every minute seemed like an hour."

I subsequently learned that Sarah's feelings are more the rule than the exception. And it's not surprising. Whenever you take independent people, accustomed to daily interactions with family, friends, or associates, and suddenly move them to a setting where the entire focus is on what's wrong with them—a setting where they have very little else to distract them—you can virtually guarantee they will suffer from boredom, depression, or both.

In Sarah's case, there was very little to occupy her time other than occasional family visits, deciding what to order for her next meal, and watching television, and although I once suggested some novels, she frequently felt too ill to concentrate for even a short time.

That's why I'm so pleased that Erica Levy Klein has chosen to write *201 Thing to Do While You're Getting Better (at Home or in the Hospital)*. I am certain that this brief, friendly book will contribute to the healing process of any patient, at any stage of recuperation.

The author describes many proven techniques for lessening pain, eliminating boredom, and dealing with the sadness that inevitably affects anyone who has ever suffered from a serious medical problem. I believe if a patient tries some of these activities and coping methods, he or she can avoid many common pitfalls of the medical world and return to complete health far more quickly.

I am hopeful this book will be made available to anyone who faces a medical problem that requires recuperation in a hospital, at home, or in an extended care facility or nursing home. As a physician, I welcome any new approach that supports the healing process, and I cannot think of a more cost-effective one than *201 Things to Do While You're Getting Better (at Home or in the Hospital)*.

—John Daniels, M.D.
Associate Clinical Professor
Washington University School of Medicine
July, 1993

WINNING THE BATTLE AGAINST PAIN AND STRESS

This is the bitterest pain among men, to have much knowledge but no power.

—Herodotus

Pain is deeper than all thought; laughter is higher than all pain.

—Elbert Hubbard

POSITIVE IS THE OPPOSITE OF NEGATIVE

**"Drink this, but stand over
there by the sink."**

2

SELF-TALK PROS AND CONS

Who do you talk most to every day? Yourself! And if you start paying attention, you'll probably be surprised at how many negative messages you're giving yourself. Are you saying things like "This is awful. I'll never make it," or "I shouldn't have to put up with this," or "I look so awful; I'm sure no one wants to be with me"?

These negative thoughts create tension. By making a conscious choice to be encouraging rather than discouraging to yourself, you can eliminate that tension. Whenever you catch yourself saying "I can't, I won't, I shouldn't," think of the railroad engine in the children's story, *The Little Engine That Could.* All the way up that steep hill, he chanted to himself, "I think I can, I think I can." And he did.

From *I Can Cope* by Judith L. Johnson, R.N., Ph.D. and Linda Klein. © 1994. CHRONIMED Publishing, Minneapolis, MN $9.95. (800) 444-5951.

WORD POWER

This exercise uses visualization to improve the power of words to convince your mind that you are healing.

1. Choose some strong words that evoke a sense of strength and healing in you. Words like yes, alive, healthy.

2. Imagine them on huge billboards all over the city, in neon lights on the side of a building, or maybe carved out of the rock on the side of a mountain.

3. Take a favorite word for each day, allowing your choice of word to be determined by what you feel you need that day.

4. Think of your word every chance you get throughout the day. See it often. Repeat the word or words to yourself as you go about your activities.

5. To reinforce this, write your word on several small cards or pieces of paper. Put them around where you will see them frequently. Each time you see them, remember your image of the word, say it to yourself, and feel it.

From *The Fine Art of Recuperation, A Guide to Surviving and Thriving After Illness, Accident or Surgery* by Regina Sara Ryan. © 1991. Jeremy P. Tarcher Publishing/Putnam Publishing Group, Los Angeles, CA $9.95 (presently out of print). For a complete catalog of Jeremy Tarcher titles, including several related to self-help and the healing process, call (213) 935-9980.

ONE FOR THE ROAD

Focus on even the smallest amount of progress in your recovery. Don't dwell on what still lies ahead of you—think about how far you've come—even if it isn't very far at all.

From Ellen Bern and Barry Mizes, St. Louis, MO.

SEEING THE OVERVIEW

Remember that compassion for yourself will be your greatest asset. Take it easy. Naturally, discouragement grows when, day after day, you don't see or feel much improvement. The fact is that sometimes things get worse just before they get better. Also, when we are anticipating a big change too fast, we often miss the subtle indications of returning strength. We easily forget that healing is not a straight-line function. Drawn on a graph, your improvement over time would look more like a jagged edge or a series of ocean waves, with numerous peaks and valleys reflecting your up days and down days. Nevertheless, the line would be projecting forward and upward. But in order to see the overall pattern, you'd have to stand back from it. Right in the middle of a crisis, one point on the line, it is hard to be aware of movement or change. The big picture is appreciated only over time.

From *The Fine Art of Recuperation, A Guide to Surviving and Thriving After Illness, Accident or Surgery* by Regina Sara Ryan. © 1991. Jeremy P. Tarcher Publishing/Putnam Publishing Group, Los Angeles, CA $9.95 (presently out of print). For a complete catalog of Jeremy Tarcher titles, including several related to self-help and the healing process, call (213) 935-9980.

5
POSITIVELY HEALTHY

You can increase the healing potential of your positive image by using positive self-talk along with it, known as positive affirmation.

An affirmation is a verbal description of a desired condition. When used repeatedly and in many different ways, affirmations get programmed into the mind just the way those destructive messages of incompetence or fear got reinforced in your earlier years.

Those who study affirmations advise certain guidelines in working with them:

• Use the present tense.
> I am...
> I see myself...
> I feel...

• Simply describe the positive outcome you expect.
> I am growing in energy and strength.
> I enjoy riding my bicycle with ease and grace.

• Avoid tentative or negative words like "might," "maybe," "hope," "will be," "don't," "not," "never."

Here are some healing affirmations to choose from or to use in composing your own:

- With every breath I grow in energy and strength.

- My mind, my body, and my soul are all working together to create healing and peace.

- I am at peace. I love and accept all of life.

- I release the old and welcome the new. Health and happiness are mine.

From *The Fine Art of Recuperation, A Guide to Surviving and Thriving After Illness, Accident or Surgery* by Regina Sara Ryan. © 1991. Jeremy P. Tarcher Publishing/Putnam Publishing Group, Los Angeles, CA $9.95 (presently out of print). For a complete catalog of Jeremy Tarcher titles, including several related to self-help and the healing process, call (213) 935-9980.

6

DON'T BE AFRAID TO SHOW YOU'RE AFRAID

Trying too hard to control your emotions as a patient can be self-defeating. It's only through emotional expression that we make our needs known—and achieve true communication. A person who cannot show pain, fright, anger, or sadness is a person with whom others cannot connect or feel empathy or love.

From *Too Perfect: When Being in Control Gets Out of Control* by Allan Mallinger, M.D., associate clinical professor of psychiatry, University of California-San Diego Medical School, Clarkson Potter Publishers, New York, NY $18. (800) 733-3000. Reprinted with permission from *Bottom Line Personal,* 330 W. 42nd St., New York, NY 10036. 24 issues per year/$49 per year or $4 per issue. (800) 274-5611.

7

IMAGINE THAT!

Although imaging techniques are a supplement to, not a substitute for, proven clinical treatment, they can be used hand-in-hand with traditional methods, drugs, and surgery to help us tap our own inborn healing powers. And they can help us better tolerate traditional medical treatments.

These basic imaging techniques were developed by a leader in the imaging field, Jose Silva:

1) Start by continuously desiring, believing, and expecting the event or state to take place. ("My high blood pressure will become normal.")

2) Relax two or three times daily, sitting quietly each time for 10 to 15 minutes in a comfortable chair, your feet on the ground. With your eyes closed, put your desired mental image on an imaginary movie screen in front of you.

3) Create your own internal "movie" of how you want the event or situation to be—your blood pressure staying level in all situations, your disease, condition, or cancer shrinking or disappearing, your breathing being deep and forceful.

4) Energize the mental image to trigger your body's own healing powers. To do so, repeat 20 times in succession, twice daily, an affirmation such as "I feel myself getting better, stronger, and healthier every day. I have only positive thoughts or assumptions, and these have an effect on every aspect of my life."

5) Open your eyes, smile, and stretch.

From *What Your Doctor Didn't Learn in Medical School ... And What You Can Do About It* by Stuart M. Berger, M.D. © 1988. William Morrow & Company, New York, NY $18.95. (212) 261-6500.

KEEPING YOUR PERSPECTIVE

When people are sick they often become very self-centered. Everything should revolve around them and their illness—or so they can easily come to believe. However, not only is such an attitude less than pleasant to live with, but it also diminishes one's ability to adjust.

From *The Diagnosis is Cancer* by Edward J. Larschan. © 1979. Bull Publishing, Menlo Park, CA $9.95. (800) 675-2855.

SMALL BLESSINGS

Because a sense of hopefulness can help speed your recuperation, end each day by mentally reviewing the things you're grateful for, no matter how small or insignificant.

10

PRIMARY FOCUS

Numerous types of religious and secular meditation offer effective methods for producing a relaxation response. The following method is an adaptation of the one developed by Herbert Bernson.

1. Lie or sit in a comfortable position where you will not be disturbed. If you're in a hospital bed, try to position it at the most comfortable angle or ask a nurse to do this for you.

2. Close your eyes and choose a center of focus. This is a word or phrase that helps shift your mind from logical, externally oriented thought to an internal, passive center of focus and stops mind-wandering when it occurs. The most common focal point is a word such as "one," "calm," or "relax." However, a short phrase can also be used such as "relax and be at peace." Many people use spiritual or religious words or phrases such as "God is with me," or "I am being watched over."

People who are very visual find it useful to develop a secondary focal point—a mental image—that forms a background for the chosen word or phrase. Examples include a calm lake or a religious figure. Some people prefer a focal point that allows them to keep their eyes open, such as a candle, picture, or statue.

3. Repeat your word or phrase each time you exhale. As you do this, it's important to adopt a positive attitude. Avoid concern about how well you are performing the technique and adopt a "let it happen" attitude. Your mind will occasionally slip away from its concentration on your word or phrase. When this happens, don't panic or abandon your practice. This is normal and to be expected. Simply redirect your mind to your breathing and continue repeating your chosen word or phrase after each exhalation.

4. Practice for 10 to 20 minutes, then open your eyes and resume your normal activities. You may open your eyes to check the time, but do not use an alarm.

From *Anxiety, Phobias and Panic: Taking Charge & Conquering Fear* by Reneau Z. Peurifoy, M.A., M.F.C.C. ©1992. Lifeskills, P.O. Box 7915, Citrus Heights, CA 95621 $12.95. (916) 723-7517.

11
TAKE THESE 8 STEPS TO PSYCHOLOGICAL STRENGTH

CHOOSE to make a plan to achieve every day—a written list of daily goals that are realistic to achieve in the time available.

APPROACH others first—be positive.

CHOOSE to have fun each day.

CHOOSE to see the positive in all things.

CHOOSE to be responsible for yourself.

CHOOSE to be in the present, don't dwell on the past.

CHOOSE to be curious and spontaneous.

CHOOSE to be in balance and seek positive responses to stresses.

From *Positive Addiction* by William Glasser, M.D. © 1988. HarperCollins, New York, NY $10. (212) 207-7000.

12

HEALTHY GOALS

For the best mental health, for the greatest emotional maturity, each individual should have *a cause, a mission, an aim in life* that is constructive and so big he or she has to keep on working on it.

From Dr. William C. Menninger, Founder, Menninger Clinic, Topeka, KS.

13
BECOME A CHAIR POTATO

Sit in a comfortable chair with your feet on the floor and your arms at your sides. Close your eyes. Breathe in, saying to yourself, "I am...," then breathe out saying, "...relaxed." Continue breathing slowly, silently repeating to yourself something such as "My hands are...warm; my feet are...warm; my forehead is...cool; my breathing is...deep and smooth; my heartbeat is ...calm and steady; I am...happy; I feel calm...and at peace."

From *Coping with Stress* by the Arthritis Foundation, P.O. Box 19000, Atlanta, GA 30326. Free. (404) 872-7100.

14

DON'T AND DOS

Sometimes being clear about what you don't want inspires you to know better what you do want. Make a list of all the ways you definitely do *not* wish to spend your time (staring out the window; talking about someone's uninteresting relative; watching TV reruns).

From *The Fine Art of Recuperation, A Guide to Surviving and Thriving After Illness, Accident or Surgery* by Regina Sara Ryan. © 1991. Jeremy P. Tarcher Publishing/Putnam Publishing Group, Los Angeles, CA $9.95 (presently out of print). For a complete catalog of Jeremy Tarcher titles, including several related to self-help and the healing process, call (213) 935-9980.

15
A FOND GLANCE BACKWARDS

Remember the 10 happiest days of your life. What were they? And why? Dwell on them for a least half an hour.

From *The Fine Art of Recuperation, A Guide to Surviving and Thriving After Illness, Accident or Surgery* by Regina Sara Ryan. © 1991. Jeremy P. Tarcher Publishing/Putnam Publishing Group, Los Angeles, CA $9.95 (presently out of print). For a complete catalog of Jeremy Tarcher titles, including several related to self-help and the healing process, call (213) 935-9980.

16

REMEMBER THE GUY IN THE BLACK HAT

Take a minute to forgive someone you dislike for his or her many transgressions against you.

17

TV OR NOT TV? THAT IS THE QUESTION

If you aren't certain as to just how therapeutic TV is in your recuperation, ask yourself these questions:

—Am I laughing more as a result of what I see on TV?

—Do I feel better about myself, about life in general, as a result of my TV watching?

—Does my pain or self-focus diminish as I watch TV?

If you can answer yes to all of the above, you are probably using TV wisely. If you answered no to any, you may want to consider other time-escaping activities that will promote your health.

From *The Fine Art of Recuperation, A Guide to Surviving and Thriving After Illness, Accident or Surgery* by Regina Sara Ryan. © 1991. Jeremy P. Tarcher Publishing/Putnam Publishing Group, Los Angeles, CA $9.95 (presently out of print). For a complete catalog of Jeremy Tarcher titles, including several related to self-help and the healing process, call (213) 935-9980.

18

THE LANGUAGE OF HEALTH

There are many ways that language can be used to affect our health—both for good and bad. Included:

- Messages we give ourselves. Whether we're aware of it or not, most of us talk to ourselves continuously.

- Pessimistic, helpless messages (I feel terrible, and there's not a thing I can do about it) tell the body to give up.

- Positive messages (I can stand this discomfort, and I will feel good again) help the body to fight illness.

From an interview with linguist Suzette Haden Elgin, Ph.D., author of *Staying Well with the Gentle Art of Verbal Self Defense.* © 1990. Prentice Hall Business and Professional Publishing, Englewood Cliffs, NJ $12.95. (201) 592-2000. Reprinted with permission from *Bottom Line Personal,* 330 W. 42nd St., New York, NY 10036. 24 issues per year/$49 per year or $4 per issue. (800) 274-5611.

COPING INSTEAD OF MOPING

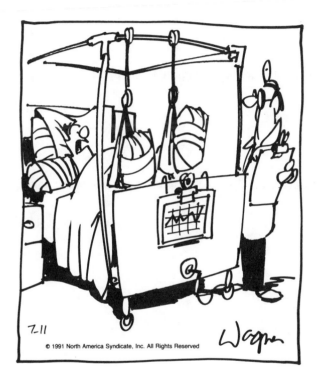

"Will I be able to play golf Saturday?"

19

ABOUT FEAR AND HIGH ANXIETY

Feeling scared and excessively anxious about your medical condition or about an upcoming procedure? Remember these two helpful thoughts:

Fear is what we *think* is going to happen.

—Elizabeth Gawain

Anxiety is the distance between the *then* and the *now.*

—Fritz Perls

QUIET ON THE SET!

One solution to the noise problems found in hospitals is a pocket-size radio and tape player with a headset. That way you can drown out the offending sounds with pleasant tones of your own, from your favorite music station to a distracting talk show. Using earplugs, such as Flents Ear Stopples®, is another solution.

21

THE NEW PATIENT FUZZIES

Here is a short list of things you can do that can help you orient yourself to being in the hospital during the first few hours:

- Ask your nurse to write down the names of the doctors and nurses who are treating you.

- Try to remember to bring along a transistor radio with headphones or a Walkman®. (Listen to the news stations that broadcast the traffic, weather, and time.)

- Ask the nurses to open the window shades. (Be aware of daytime and nighttime.)

- Ask for paper and pens or pencils and a clipboard. Place a pillow under the clipboard to make writing more comfortable.

- Get your room TV turned on, but don't be surprised if the noise level and the daytime programs are not helpful for your new "patient" feelings. The same game show you enjoyed at home may annoy you when you are in a hospital room.

From *Pregnancy Bedrest: A Guide for the Pregnant Woman and Her Family* by Susan H. Johnston, M.S.W. and Deborah A. Kraut, M.I.L.R. © 1990. Henry Holt, New York, NY $14.95. (212) 886-9200.

SKIMPY FASHIONS

If wearing a hospital robe with its peekaboo lines embarrasses you, don't wear it all the time. Or wear two of them. Put one on their way, with the open part to the rear; put the other one on the way normal human beings wear a robe with the open section up front. That way the pokers and probers can still get to wherever they need to delve and you have retained a certain level of modesty. Slip into your pajamas when you stroll or when you see visitors. Short-sleeve sleepwear is preferable to allow a blood pressure cuff to be slung around your arm at a moment's notice. Put the hospital gown on again before going to bed for the night if your own sleepwear could interfere with necessary access to your body by the hospital staff or with your comfort in bed.

From *Take This Book to the Hospital With You* by Charles B. Inlander and Ed Weiner. © 1991. Pantheon Books/Random House, New York, NY by People's Medical Society, $14.95. (800) 733-3000.

23

GET ANGRY/GET HOPEFUL

Both anger and hope are healthy responses to illness. They're expressions of defiance, antidotes to fear and pain, displays of belief in the future. When your weakened body seems a burden fit to be forsaken, anger and hope are the engines that drive you to live.

Watch out, though, anger and hope can also be false friends who will neatly undo you unless you are careful to keep them in check. Anger is self-defeating when:

- You let yourself sulk and abandon all pleasure, until finally it seems you have nothing to live for.

- You lash out at others who'd like to be helpful but who finally withdraw out of fear that they merely annoy you.

- You petulantly cancel your medical appointments or refuse to be treated, in order to punish the doctor (or yourself).

- You undermine your spirit with constant complaints and fruitless laments.

Even hope, which is so much less threatening, can mock and abuse you if:

- You behave unrealistically by engaging, for example, in arduous activities for which you aren't fit.

- You trust in blind luck and refuse to be bothered with exercise, diets, and drugs the doctor has ordered.

- You grasp at a miracle cure that is proffered by quacks, while spurning a thoroughly safe and effective conventional treatment.

According to the proverb, hope is the physician of each new misery—but only if it doesn't cause you miseries anew. When handled sensibly, anger and hope can protect you from losing respect for yourself. And since self-respect is medicine as strong as a drug, it's a valuable commodity to foster.

From *You Can Make It Back: Coping With Serious Illness* by Paul M. Levitt and Elissa S. Guralnick. © 1985. Facts on File Publications, New York, NY $16.95. Currently out of print, still available in many libraries. (212) 683-2244.

24

SLAYING THE BEAST OF DEPRESSION

If you're depressed, the first thing to do is allow yourself to experience your depression to the fullest. You may need a break from being cheerful, brave, and under control. Depression isn't all that bad. It may give you a chance to "catch your second breath." You have spent a lot of energy denying your anger and guilt—or your guilt about being angry. When you're at the bottom, there's only one way to go, and that's up!

In the cycle of adjustment, you may experience anger, denial, bargaining, depression, and acceptance. Depression is like hitting the wall of reality, experiencing the pain and tears, "letting it all hang out." It is the mechanism by which you are able to get on with life.

Key One: Allow yourself to experience the pain and reality where you are—at the bottom. Don't fight it or belittle yourself for being there. Know it's part of a process and need not last forever.

Key Two: Look below the surface to see what emotions are there. List what you may possibly feel angry, anxious, or guilty about.

Key Three: Get to know yourself, your thoughts, and what triggers your depression.

Key Four: Don't be ashamed to cry. Allow yourself to shed some tears.

Key Five: Some type of exertion on a regular basis (a few times a week) may help break chronic depression/fatigue scenarios.

Key Six: Recognize that depression may be more prevalent during the winter months or on rainy days, a widely accepted fact.

Key Seven: Good nutrition and a well-balanced diet may slow or even help reverse a downward spiral of depression.

Key Eight: Identify your key support people and let them know when you need them.

Key Nine: Deliberately plan an activity or treat that you really enjoy for those days when you are most prone to depression.

Key Ten: Establish schedules. Write down things you need to do, and check them off when done. Stay involved with others, whether by mail, phone, newspapers, or television.

Key Eleven: When experiencing increased pain or depression, try to realistically fathom which is which by recognizing they sometimes go hand in hand. Try to treat the problem from both directions, as pain or depression, and see which approach works best. Both entities can cause and make the other worse.

From *Successful Living with Chronic Illness* by Kathleen Lewis. © 1989. Avery Publishing Group, Garden City Park, NY $10. To order: (404) 491-6850.

25
PICTURE THIS

Do you have a photograph of yourself taken during one of your "peak" periods of health and vitality? Get it out and keep it around. Look at it. Comb magazines for shots of healthy people. Clip those and put them up. See yourself in the pictures.

From *The Fine Art of Recuperation, A Guide to Surviving and Thriving After Illness, Accident or Surgery* by Regina Sara Ryan. © 1991. Jeremy P. Tarcher Publishing/Putnam Publishing Group, Los Angeles, CA $9.95 (presently out of print). For a complete catalog of Jeremy Tarcher titles, including several related to self-help and the healing process, call (213) 935-9980.

26
RX: LAUGHTER

Just when we need humor most, it is often hardest to come by—amid anxious family and friends, strange clinical settings, and overall uncertainty. How then do you introduce more laughter into your life? By renting a videotape machine for 3 months, along with every classic film comedy available. (I got into Marx Brothers, Three Stooges, and Charlie Chaplin marathons.) TV sitcoms could easily work the same way.

Also, friends can give you all sorts of humorous reading material—anything from Andy Rooney and spoofs of law and lawyers to a volume of X-rated limericks. At a very minimum, films and books can raise your spirits and keep you entertained—and that itself is a form of therapy.

From *The Diagnosis is Cancer* by Edward J. Larschan. © 1979. Bull Publishing, Menlo Park, CA $9.95. (800) 676-2855.

27
HEALTHSTYLES OF THE RICH AND FAMOUS

Remember some famous people who produced prolifically despite chronic physical problems:

Franklin Roosevelt led the nation and vigorously pursued wartime victory while confined to a wheelchair following adult-onset polio.

Barbara Jordan, the Texas congresswoman, served the public well despite being in a wheelchair because of a neuromuscular disease.

John Kennedy campaigned for the presidency and served in that office with often intense chronic pain as a result of a back injury.

Beethoven wrote his final works as his hearing faded and ultimately deserted him.

The renowned astrophysicist **Stephen Hawking** wrote his best-selling *On the Origins of the Universe* while paralyzed by a serious neurologic disease.

Elizabeth Browning, bedridden with a back injury, wrote enduring romantic poetry from her sickroom.

Florence Nightingale's disabling lung disease didn't stop her from giving advice to the military authorities on how to set up wartime medical services.

Proust wrote his brilliant works under the stress of a disabling respiratory disease.

Robert Louis Stevenson gave us the pleasure of his adventure novels written from the confines of his sickbed.

Martha Graham, with severe arthritis, brought soaring joy to millions with her innovative dance choreography.

And **Mickey Mantle** slugged 536 home runs despite the intense chronic pain and discomfort of injured and battered knees.

From *Healing the Body Betrayed: A Self-Paced, Self-Help Guide to Regaining Psychological Control of Your Chronic Illness* by Robert A. Klein, Ph.D. and Marcia Goodman Landau, Ph.D. © 1992. CHRONIMED Publishing, Minneapolis, MN $12.95. (800) 444-5951.

28
TOURS AND DETOURS

Some hospitals have a special lounge area for patients or a veranda for good-weather days. Go there for a change of scene. Go to these places with your visitors so they don't have to see you in bed. Sit in these havens to think, to knit, to read (the light is probably better there, too), or to nap. For an hour or so you can put to one side the fact you are in a hospital.

If your hospital has no sitting areas for patients, get up and walk around anyway (assuming you have your doctor's permission). When you get out of bed and step out of your room, you not only improve your constitution, you also make a clear declaration of independence.

From *Take This Book to the Hospital With You* by Charles B. Inlander and Ed Weiner. © 1991. Pantheon Books/Random House, New York, NY by People's Medical Society, $14.95. (800) 733-3000.

PROFESSIONAL PROBLEM SOLVER

Both to reduce lawsuits and minimize disruptions, many hospitals have a patient advocate or ombudsman whose main job is to solve problems quickly and smoothly. When you are unable to solve a problem yourself, call this person, whose telephone number will be prominently displayed in the literature you are given upon admission.

From *The Diagnosis is Cancer* by Edward J. Larschan. © 1979. Bull Publishing, Menlo Park, CA $9.95. (800) 676-2855.

MENTAL VACATIONS

Sometimes simply letting your mind wander or "go on vacation" will help reduce your stress. Assuming your recuperation lets you get out of doors, here are a few suggestions from the Arthritis Foundation. (You can also invent your own!)

- Watch a sunset
- Take your shoes off and walk in the grass
- Sit in a park on a warm, sunny day and listen to the birds
- Sit in front of the fire in the fireplace
- Gaze at fish in the pet store or at an aquarium

31
A HEALTHY YELL

You may have learned by now that certain behaviors are expected of "good patients," and that strong emotions that rock the boat of normal routine are not among them. You may fear emotional release because it will upset those around you, and you may be right. Those who have never done it themselves may feel threatened. They may fear that you are getting worse, when more likely the opposite is true. Your emotional expression may simply be triggering their own tears and fears. But don't let that stop you. There are lots of "safe" ways to let yourself go that won't get you labeled for life but will keep you in touch with a sense of control in the process.

One method is to try this "silent scream" technique when you are alone or in the company of someone you trust. Open your mouth and let loose with your breath, your facial contortions, your vigorous body movements. An unvocalized scream or cry or even laughter can work every bit as well as a vocalized one. Try it. Or try screaming into a pillow. Allow 10 minutes for the process, no more. When the time is up, just stop and turn your attention to something else, or snuggle up with your teddy bear, if you have one, and take a nap.

From *The Fine Art of Recuperation, A Guide to Surviving and Thriving After Illness, Accident or Surgery* by Regina Sara Ryan. © 1991. Jeremy P. Tarcher Publishing/Putnam Publishing Group, Los Angeles, CA $9.95 (presently out of print). For a complete catalog of Jeremy Tarcher titles, including several related to self-help and the healing process, call (213) 935-9980.

32

REDEFINING YOURSELF

Try not to think of yourself as a sick person. Think of yourself as a healthy person who on occasion gets sick.

From *Healing the Body Betrayed: A Self-Paced, Self-Help Guide to Regaining Psychological Control of Your Chronic Illness* by Robert A. Klein, Ph. D. and Marcia Goodman Landau, Ph.D. © 1992. CHRONIMED Publishing. Minneapolis, MN $12.95. (800) 444-5951.

ACCEPTING YOUR OWN INVITATION

Acceptance is like a see-saw. Part of you wants to get on with life as it is now, and another part wants to stay with the loss. It takes a lot of time, patience, love, determination, and understanding. Acceptance is a day-by-day experience, as things are continually changing. But having reached the following hallmarks once gives promise that you can continue to capitalize on them. Here are some hallmarks of acceptance that are usually evident to the chronically ill and those around them:

1. It is no longer necessary to focus on the illness or one's self.

2. You begin to see the needs of others again.

3. The illness blends in as only part of your total identity, so everyone doesn't have to know about it.

4. You no longer go to great lengths to hide the illness. It is no longer considered a painful fact that must be concealed.

5. Illness' effects become contained so they do not affect all situations in life.

6. You are able to identify with people who have similar conditions and acknowledge changes in yourself.

7. You develop or regain a well-rounded life that includes old interests as well as some possible new ones.

8. You feel emotional as well as intellectual acceptance.

9. Feelings of bitterness, defensiveness, and anger are released. You no longer see yourself as a victim but as a participant and assume responsibility for yourself.

10. Fears become more realistic instead of a generalized, consuming anxiety.

11. You accept yourself, shed self-pity, and become comfortable with yourself and those around you.

12. You accept the reality of your limitations and learn to ask for help in an assertive way—not aggressively, not whimpering or complaining, but bargaining your limitations.

13. You try to see humor in your situation and learn to laugh and play again.

14. You set new goals when old ones are no longer realistic.

15. The reach for acceptance seems to connect with the idea that hope is returning.

16. You see yourself as being no different than others, only an "average Joe or Josephine" handling problems as well as possible—no martyr, saint, or anyone special.

17. You are able to identify with the similarities of others and not just with your differences.

18. You see yourself as a person of value as you are right now.

19. You learn to listen to, understand, and trust yourself.

From *Successful Living with Chronic Illness* by Kathleen Lewis. © 1989. Avery Publishing Group, Garden City Park, NY $10. To order: (404) 491-6850.

LET YOUR "GUARDIAN ANGEL" WATCH OVER YOU

In *Dreaming in the Dark,* author Starhawk describes two voices that "speak" to us inside our own head. One is the voice of the self-hater who demands, criticizes, judges everything, and finds us wanting. It challenges us to do something right away. The other voice is that of the guardian—really the voice of reason, the voice of balance, the voice of God. This voice speaks of what is necessary for healing in practical terms. It supports and encourages but doesn't coddle. It suggests instead the gentle path of patience and self-acceptance, of one step at a time.

The easiest way to make immediate use of your guardian is to imagine that you are advising someone else in your exact situation. What would you tell your best friends to do if they felt the way you felt and were being demanding toward themselves? What would you say if he or she had gone through the accident or surgery or illness that you had and needed some emotional support right now? There you have it. Take your own advice. Be easy on yourself, and listen to your own "guardian" angel.

From *The Fine Art of Recuperation, A Guide to Surviving and Thriving After Illness, Accident or Surgery* by Regina Sara Ryan. © 1991 Jeremy P. Tarcher Publishing/Putnam Publishing Group, Los Angeles, CA $9.95 (presently out of print). For a complete catalog of Jeremy Tarcher titles, including several related to self-help and the healing process, call (213) 935-9980.

35
THAT TOUCH OF HOME

If you're in the hospital or other alien surroundings, something old and familiar—something that looks and feels like home—will be a welcome emotional support. Your own pajamas or nightgown; your own pillow and bedspread; those family photos; your coffee mug; your teddy bear. Ask friends or family to help make your environment a place of healing, not just enduring. Small changes will make a tremendous difference in your ability to sustain the emotional ups and downs that life delivers .

From *The Fine Art of Recuperation, A Guide to Surviving and Thriving After Illness, Accident or Surgery* by Regina Sara Ryan. © 1991. Jeremy P. Tarcher Publishing/Putnam Publishing Group, Los Angeles, CA $9.95 (presently out of print). For a catalog of Jeremy Tarcher titles, including several related to self-help and the healing process, call (213) 935-9980.

36

SMALL CHANGES/BIG DIFFERENCES

Sometimes the tiniest modification, like a different bedspread, or a colored light bulb, can make a tremendous change in the entire atmosphere of the room you're recuperating in at home. Keep this in mind as you read over the following possibilities:

- Plants, flowers, and more plants. You can grow an herb garden in an empty egg carton or old ice cube tray on your window. Herbs grow fast and smell great.

- Living things. Perhaps it's time to get that pet you've always wanted. A kitten? A few fish? A bird.

- Posters and pictures. Posters can be educational as well as decorative. You can lie flat on your back and study a map of the world, great wines of California, botany, or anatomy placed on the ceiling or wall nearest you. Many public libraries will allow you to check out a painting. Change your pictures or murals regularly, or move them around to gain a whole new appreciation of them.

- Let there be light. Vary the light in the room by changing the intensity or color of light bulbs or by moving lamps around.

- Color. Experiment and play as much as possible with the effects of colors in bedspreads, tablecloths, wall hangings, and window treatments.

- Fragrance. Incense, if used sparingly, can totally change the environment for the better, especially if your room tends to smell "sickly." Room fresheners are available at all grocery stores. How about a drop or two of scented oil for the light bulbs?

- Your bed. Make your bed as colorful and sensuous as possible. Give special attention to the colors and textures of bedding. If you have never used cotton flannel sheets, treat yourself. Comfortable even in the warmest weather, they provide a nurturing, soothing feeling.

- Toys. A bulletin board or blackboard is handy to have around. So is a stuffed animal. Or some exercise equipment, assuming your doctor says it's OK for you to use it.

- What else? Don't be stingy. This is your vacation, albeit a forced one. Splurge a little. The money you spend enlivening your environment may well decrease what you will have to spend in painkillers and other drugs. So pleasure yourself.

From *The Fine Art of Recuperation, A Guide to Surviving and Thriving After Illness, Accident or Surgery* by Regina Sara Ryan. © 1991. Jeremy P. Tarcher Publishing/Putnam Publishing Group, Los Angeles, CA $9.95 (presently out of print). For a complete catalog of Jeremy Tarcher titles, including several related to self-help and the healing process, call (213) 935-9980.

TECHNICALLY SPEAKING

If you're recuperating at home, take advantage of self-help devices that can make dressing, bathing, and housecleaning easier. Many of these are available through mail-order catalogs such as Comfortably Yours, (201) 368-0400, or medical supply outlets.

From *Coping with Pain—The Battle Half Won* by the Arthritis Foundation, P.O. Box 19000, Atlanta, GA 30326 Free. (404) 872-7100.

38

WRITING OUT RECUPERATION

There is no one right way to start a "recuperation journal." But here are some helpful suggestions to get you started:

- Tell the story of your illness or accident. Start at the beginning and record everything you know about it. Do this again in a week and see if your outlook is different in the two stories.

- Have a dialogue with your illness, a part of your body, or another part of your mind. Give that part a voice and a name of its own. Ask it about the crisis you are experiencing, why it is happening now, and what it has to teach you. Be courageously candid.

- Start a conversation with a wise teacher, a spiritual leader, a famous doctor, or anyone else you know can help you in your recuperation. Communicate your deepest feelings, your needs, and your fears. Then write a reply to yourself from your new friend or teacher. Give yourself advice. Love yourself.

- Play with the past. Recall the three most important decisions you've ever made, but suppose that in each case you made another choice. What difference would that have made? Tell your life story now, incorporating those three new choices.

- Dream up the future. Imagine that 10 years from now you meet yourself on a park bench. The person you meet is magnificent: healthy, strong, gentle, compassionate, successful. Describe in detail what you're like. Have a conversation with yourself revealing how you managed to turn out so beautifully.

- Go on a cruise. Create a fantasy of the most pleasurable confinement you can imagine. Pretend you're the only passenger on a small cruise ship crossing the Pacific

Ocean. The trip will take 3 weeks. You have a tiny state-room and a lounge chair on the deck. Write about what you will do to spend your time.

- Write or compose poetry. Consider the following ideas.

  - Reflections. List all the things you remember about your childhood home and some of the pleasant things you did there. Your list becomes your poem.

  - Love. Look around your room and choose any object that catches your eye. Now create an explanation of why love is like that object.

  - If. Begin with the statement "If I had my life to live over again, I would. . . "

From *The Fine Art of Recuperation, A Guide to Surviving and Thriving After Illness, Accident or Surgery* by Regina Sara Ryan. © 1991. Jeremy P. Tarcher Publishing/Putnam Publishing Group, Los Angeles, CA $9.95 (presently out of print). For a complete catalog of Jeremy Tarcher titles, including several related to self-help and the healing process, call (213) 935-9980.

39

ROOM TO GROW (BETTER)

Use the following questions to begin making lists of any and all ways in which you can modify your surrounding to encourage restfulness, security, stimulation, and health.

- Is there enough open space in this setting? If not, what can be removed to allow for it?

- Is there too much space? If so, what would I like to fill it with? (Space is not simply empty floor area. Look at the walls and ceiling as well. Are they too busy, too bare, or too boring? What needs to change, if anything?)

- Does this room reflect the richness and beauty of my personality?

- What colors are "healing colors" for me? Do I have enough of them?

- Would green plants or flowers be able to thrive in this environment? (If they couldn't, how can you expect to?)

- Are there healthy, interesting, and inspiring things to look at in this environment?

- What is the "audio" environment like? Noise levels? Opportunities for music? What kinds? What music feels healing to you?

- What does this place smell like? Is this healing for you? What is?

- If you could design the most perfect environment for your recovery, what would it be like? What colors would you choose, what furniture? What sort of lighting, what kind of access or vulnerability to sound? Would you have living things? What's the view from the window? How accessible are the things you need?

From *The Fine Art of Recuperation, A Guide to Surviving and Thriving After Illness, Accident or Surgery* by Regina Sara Ryan. © 1991. Jeremy P. Tarcher Publishing/Putnam Publishing Group, Los Angeles, CA $9.95 (presently out of print). For a complete catalog of Jeremy Tarcher titles, including several related to self-help and the healing process, call (213) 935-9980.

WORKING ON LEISURE

Force yourself to get back in the swing of leisure activities as soon as possible. Can't think of what you'd like to do? Here are some suggestions:

- Bake a cake
- Build a doghouse or cat stand
- Paint your own portrait
- Take a walk and reacquaint yourself with a favorite area or park
- Put in a new bush or nurture a new plant
- Cook a gourmet dinner from recipes in a magazine
- Collect stamps or rocks
- Sew a new outfit or work on a craft project
- Start a new social group
- Take in a movie
- Visit an old friend
- Join a new club

From *I Can Cope* by Judith L. Johnson, R.N., Ph.D. and Linda Klein. © 1994. CHRONIMED Publishing, Minneapolis, MN $9.95. (800) 444-5951.

41

MOVING ONWARD AND UPWARD

Simple isometric exercises like the ones below will help you maintain and increase your range of motion. However, always consult your physician before undertaking any exercise during recuperation. When lying down and looking straight ahead, do the following:

— Place the heel of your hand on your forehead and push your forehead against your hand.

— Place the palm of your hand against the back of your head, and push your head backward against the force of your hand.

— Place the palm of your right hand against the right side of your head and push your head sideward, resisting the pressure of your hand. Do the same for your left side.

— Clench your teeth, raise your head slightly, and forcefully pull the corners of your mouth outward and down.

While in a sitting position:

— Put the palms of your hands together and forcefully push them toward each other.

— Clasp your hands together and then try to forcefully pull them apart.

From *I Can Cope* by Judith L. Johnson, R.N., Ph. D. and Linda Klein. © 1994. CHRONIMED Publishing, Minneapolis, MN $9.95. (800) 444-5951.

DRESSED FOR THE BEST

If you have limited range of motion, the following suggestions make dressing yourself more comfortable:

- Do as much as possible while seated in an armchair.
- Put your weak arm or leg in your clothing first when dressing.
- Take your strong arm or leg out of your clothing first when undressing.
- If you're a woman, buy an attractive loose-fitting lounge coat or caftan, if you're not yet wearing street clothes.

From *I Can Cope* by Judith L. Johnson, R.N., Ph.D. and Linda Klein. © 1994. CHRONIMED Publishing, Minneapolis, MN $9.95. (800) 444-5951.

BATHING BEAUTY

To make independent bathing easier, try these strategies:

- Install grab bars next to the tub if there aren't some there already.

- Use a bath seat for sitting in the tub.

- If you want to take a shower without standing up, use a portable shower head and a bath seat.

- Install a device known as a raised toilet seat. It makes it easier to stand up after using the toilet and is particularly useful for people with hip pain.

From *I Can Cope* by Judith L. Johnson, R.N., Ph.D. and Linda Klein. © 1994. CHRONIMED Publishing, Minneapolis, MN $9.95. (800) 444-5951.

44
IT'S A DRAW!

— Divide a blank piece of paper in half. Draw yourself as you feel now on one side. On the other side, draw yourself as you will be when you are fully well. Don't feel confined to drawing your image as a recognizable body. Be free to portray yourself in an abstract form.

— Draw your illness or accident. Again, use abstractions and symbols as you wish. Now draw the healing agents that are eliminating the illness or accident. Show interaction between the two.

— Depict aliveness, love, forgiveness, or gratitude.

— Draw the interplay of life and death, health and disease, joy and sorrow.

— Draw any feeling you are currently enduring: aloneness, fear, anxiety, sadness, doubt, guilt, pain.

— Draw the world as you see it now. Then draw it as you wish it to be.

— Draw an ally—a friend, angel, animal, or symbol that represents support, companionship, and unconditional love.

— Draw laughter, hilarity, silliness, absurdity.

— Draw a fantasy place of comfort and safety.

— Draw a dream sequence.

— Draw your own face, then have a conversation with it.

From *The Fine Art of Recuperation, A Guide to Surviving and Thriving After Illness, Accident or Surgery* by Regina Sara Ryan. © 1991. Jeremy P. Tarcher Publishing/Putnam Publishing Group, Los Angeles, CA $9.95 (presently out of print). For a complete catalog of Jeremy Tarcher titles, including several related to self-help and the healing process, call (213) 935-9980.

45

LOOKING BETTER AND FEELING BETTER

In the beginning stages of an illness, or in the shock phase of an accident, you'll have all you can do just to meet your survival needs for sleep, nourishment, and pain control. When that phase is over and you itch to start moving again, begin a short daily routine of self-care for looking and feeling better. Among other things, it provides another way to structure some of the endless time you have on your hands.

There is a fine line to be walked as you attend to your physical appearance in bed or around the house as you recuperate. You certainly do not need to burden yourself with looking "good as new." In fact, if you try, you will probably be pushing too hard. On the other hand, there is a definite energy attached to cleanliness, to order, and especially to a bright, warm color. What you see when you look in the mirror is going to affect the way you feel.

Here are a few ways to enhance your body image, to lift your spirits, and to make good use of your time as you recuperate:

- Get a haircut, change the style. Even asking a friend to simply wash and dry your hair will provide a welcome change.

- Get a manicure or pedicure.

- Get a foot massage.

- Attend to your teeth and gums.

- Wear warm, lively, or tranquil colors to suit your moods. Choose colors that bring out a healthy glow in your skin tone and experience how that elevates your spirits.

- Dress for energy in a jogging suit and bright shirt rather than crumpled pajamas. Or put on an attractive nightgown or nightshirt.

- Do facial exercises to soften lines and tone muscles.

- Give yourself a facial massage. Knead, slap, stroke, and roll the skin on your face (gently around the eyes). Consider that you're trying to wake up all the cells and increase circulation throughout the face.

- If your doctor says it's OK, treat your skin to a moisturizing lotion or cream, or even an oil treatment.

- Try something just for fun. Try repainting your cast, putting on a hat or brightly colored scarf, or adding a temporary tattoo to a place where only the doctor will find it. One man donned a gorilla mask whenever somber visitors were expected.

From *The Fine Art of Recuperation, A Guide to Surviving and Thriving After Illness, Accident or Surgery* by Regina Sara Ryan. © 1991. Jeremy P. Tarcher Publishing/Putnam Publishing Group, Los Angeles, CA $9.95 (presently out of print). For a complete catalog of Jeremy Tarcher titles, including several related to self-help and the healing process, call (213) 935-9980.

BRIGHT SPOTS

Experienced "bed-lyers" will tell you that adding a bit of color or aliveness to yourself or your immediate environment will go a long way in helping to brighten your spirits. Use green plants or other living things—a bird in a cage, an aquarium of fish. Try varying the light in the room by removing curtains or changing light bulbs. Ask a friend to hang a new poster or picture on your wall. The possibilities are endless.

From *The Fine Art of Recuperation, A Guide to Surviving and Thriving After Illness, Accident or Surgery* by Regina Sara Ryan. © 1991. Jeremy P. Tarcher Publishing/Putnam Publishing Group, Los Angeles, CA $9.95 (presently out of print). For a complete catalog of Jeremy Tarcher titles, including several related to self-help and the healing process, call (213) 935-9980.

IF YOU HAVE TO LEAVE WORK PERMANENTLY

Professionals offer many tips for people who must leave the work force because of an illness or injury:

- Choose a doctor you like and rely on him or her for encouragement, not just prescriptions.

- Expect emotional changes. Seek counseling or develop a caring network by contacting support groups. (See the *Encyclopedia of Associations* at your library as a starting point.)

- Contact the local Center for Independent Living to obtain peer counseling and learn how to maintain independence.

- Find out what insurance benefits your employer, union, or association provides.

- If applying for Social Security disability, contact the Social Security Administration for information. Also, try to manage the negative effects of the disability qualification process by mentally separating yourself from it. Remind yourself that nothing is meant to be a personal attack on you.

- Nurture a compassionate circle of friends.

- Create a daily structure that includes exercise, particularly an aquatics program, walking, or a set of exercises designed for you.

- Go back to school. Classes are also available for those at home through both local institutions or correspondence schools.

- If at home, build a telephone network with peers, friends, and relatives. Also, continue socialization by inviting friends over for a potluck dinner once a month. (You could ask each guest to bring food and someone you don't know.)

- If rehabilitation is possible, start a home business or try computer, secretarial, or office work, telephone sales, counseling, or childcare. Contact the local Department of Rehabilitation Services to learn about suitable vocations.

- Prepare for eventual retirement by developing hobbies and interests outside of work.

From *Arthritis Today: The Magazine of Help and Hope.* September-October, 1990. 1314 Spring St., N.W., Atlanta, GA 30309. The magazine is available free to those who join the Arthritis Foundation. (404) 872-7100.

PAINKICKERS

"I think I'd like to explore some
treatment alternatives."

48

MEDICATING YOUR PAIN

What can you do if you feel you're not getting enough pain medication?

- Discuss with your doctor your fear of or concern about pain and your desire for adequate medication to control pain. Pain is a complex symptom. Not all of it is physical in origin; much derives from anxiety, a sense of hopelessness, family stress, fear, and spiritual concerns. These feelings can lower your threshold for pain, thereby creating the perception of more and more pain. With your doctor, discover the cause of your pain.

- Be sure to ask what the adverse side effects of the painkilling drugs are. A June 1988 article in *Postgraduate Medicine* states pain control measures sometimes failed because the patient could not anticipate the adverse side effects.

- Communicate as honestly as you can the extent of your pain. Some experts recommend that doctors ask two key questions: Does the medicine ever take away the pain completely? According to Robert G. Twycross and Sylvia A. Lack in *Symptom Control in Far Advanced Cancer: Pain Relief,* if the answer is no, then the dose should be increased. Does the pain return before the next dose of medicine? If yes, then the dose should also be increased. But don't wait for your doctor to ask the questions. Give him or her the answers right away.

- Discuss with your physician the alternative therapies for pain relief—for example, biofeedback, hypnosis, relaxation techniques, and acupuncture. While they may not work in your case, they have in many others.

From an interview with linguist Suzette Haden Elgin, Ph.D., author of *Staying Well with the Gentle Art of Verbal Self Defense.* © 1990. Prentice Hall Business and Professional Publishing, Englewood Cliffs, NJ $12.95. (201) 592-2000. Reprinted with permission from *Bottom Line Personal,* 330 W. 42nd St., New York, NY 10036. 24 issues per year/$49 per year or $4 per issue. (800) 274-5611.

ACUTE VS. CHRONIC AT THE OK CORRAL

Although all pain feels awful, it may help to remember there is a big difference between acute and chronic pain.

Acute Pain is an unpleasant sensation associated with an injury such as a cut or surgical incision. Usually acute pain is short-lived, and it most often goes away when the injury or illness is healed or cured.

Chronic Pain is a persistent pain that continues long after healing has occurred. For many people, chronic pain stops being a symptom of the disease and becomes a problem itself.

For people who suffer from chronic pain, a pain management clinic can often offer a dynamic alternative to passive acceptance of pain. People with chronic pain have many differing needs. A pain clinic can offer innovative methods of treatments and information and support from a variety of disciplines. Types of disorders commonly treated at a pain clinic or pain management center include:

- back pain

- muscle contraction (tension) headaches

- migraine (vascular) headaches

- post-herpetic neuralgia—an excruciating pain which sometimes appears as the aftermath of an attack of shingles

- tic douloureux (painful tic), which affects the trigeminal nerve of the face

- causalgia and reflex sympathetic dystrophy—burning pain resulting from an injury to peripheral nerves

- hypertension

- heart problems

- incontinence

- stress-related illnesses

- cancer pain

- arthritis pain

- pain from TMJ

- anxiety and panic disorders

Adapted from *Solving the Problem of Pain.* The Pain Center at DePaul Hospital, St. Louis, MO. (314) 344-7019.

50
BEATING PAIN AT ITS OWN GAME

If you're plagued with either acute or chronic pain, instead of telling yourself, "I can't bear this," substitute the thought, "I can stand this pain for 15 minutes."

Then spend the 15 minutes doing something you enjoy—gardening, listening to music, absorbing yourself in a challenging task or project. At the end of 15 minutes, you're likely to find that the pain has diminished or is gone.

If not, say, "I can stand this pain for another 15 minutes." You'll notice the pain ebbs and flows. This attitude enables you to go on with your life, instead of focusing your life around the pain.

Another way to cope with pain is to keep a journal. Describe what the pain feels like and what sets it off. Give it a name. Compare it with something else that has a familiar distinguishable feature.

> Example: My pain is like an earthquake — sudden and unpredictable.

As you define your pain and give it boundaries, you'll see it less as an overwhelming force that's controlling you, and more as an object...which you can control.

From an interview with linguist Suzette Haden Elgin, Ph.D., author of *Staying Well with the Gentle Art of Verbal Self Defense.* © 1990. Prentice Hall Business and Professional Publishing, Englewood Cliffs, NJ $12.95. (201) 592-2000. Reprinted with permission from *Bottom Line Personal,* 330 W. 42nd St., New York, NY 10036. 24 issues per year/$49 per year or $4 per issue. (800) 274-5611.

51
CALMING PAIN DOWN

STEP ONE:
When you first feel pain, don't panic. If you panic, the pain will surely increase. Panic and tension tend to increase pain.

STEP TWO:
Don't let fear get the best of you. Calmly assess the situation. Be aware of where the pain is located, whether it is new or old, and how severe it is. Try not to let your imagination get the best of you. Don't anticipate the worst! Statements such as "I just know it's going to get worse," should be strictly avoided.

STEP THREE:
Inhale deeply through your nose. Try to take the air all the way down into your stomach and expand your stomach to fill your lungs completely. Exhale slowly through your mouth, trying to empty your lungs and stomach completely. As you exhale, your stomach should contract. Relax and repeat twice.

Now inhale slowly through your nose to the count of two. Hold your breath to the count of three and exhale through your mouth to the count of two. Relax to the count of four. Repeat this pattern for several minutes. (You may find that using the count of three, four, or five will be best for you.)

STEP FOUR:
Get into the most comfortable position possible and close your eyes. Take a deep breath, holding it for a count of three and letting it out slowly for a count of three. Take another deep breath (count of three). Do this five times, and on the fifth deep breath, as you inhale, repeat to yourself the words "I am." Hold the deep breath for a brief count of two or three, and as you exhale, say to yourself the words, "Pain-Free." The repetition of the words "I am ... Pain-Free" in sequence with your breathing will immediately counter-act the fear or panic that generally starts at the onset of pain.

From *Power Over Your Pain Without Drugs* by Neal Olshan. © 1980. Beaufort Books/SBN Publishing, New York, NY $12.95. (212) 727-0190.

52
NEW DEVELOPMENTS IN PAIN CONTROL

Although medicating pain is always an option, you may want to ask your doctor about these new approaches to pain control:

Behavioral Therapy: biofeedback, relaxation training, or stress-management programs are often used to relieve pain, reduce muscle spasm, and diminish stress.

Transcutaneous Nerve Stimulation (TENS): non-painful electrical impulses that "block out the pain." TENS consists of a small battery-operated device that can stimulate nerve fibers through the skin to diminish pain.

Acupuncture: as an alternative to TENS, electrical stimulation of acupuncture points is sometimes performed.

Rehabilitation Services: physical and occupational therapy treatments that may include exercise, whirlpool, ultrasound, massage, and manipulation.

Nerve Blocks: an injection of local anesthetic, with or without cortisone-like medicines, around nerves or into joints. These may act to reduce swelling, irritation, muscle spasms, or abnormal nerve transmissions that can cause pain.

Cryoanalgesia: freezing the affected area to reduce pain. Normally, it is used for pain generated from the chest wall.

Implantable Analgesia: time-released mechanism for releasing pain-relieving medication. The implant will deliver minimal amounts of pain-relieving medication into the the spinal cord. Implantable epidural stimulators are also available for blocking lower-body pain.

Adapted from West County Pain Control Center, St. Louis, MO. (314) 567-0402 and The Pain Management Center, Christian Hospital Northeast, St. Louis, MO. (314) 355-2500, ext. 2500.

53

A BILL OF RIGHTS FOR PEOPLE IN PAIN

People who do best in coping with their pain believe in their rights. To assert these rights in all situations is a matter of belief in yourself and your ability to control pain. Many people write these simple sentences on a piece of paper or card and carry their "bill of rights" wherever they go.

1. I have the *Right* to live a full and happy life.

2. I have the *Right* not to have to prove my pain.

3. I have the *Right* to control decisions regarding my pain.

4. I have the *Right* to demand appropriate medical attention.

5. I have the *Right* to be alone when I choose.

6. I have the *Right* to refuse requests that may increase my pain.

7. I have the *Right* to pain relief.

From *The Scottsdale Pain Relief Program* by Dr. Neal H. Olshan. © 1987. Beaufort Books/SBN Publishing, New York, NY $16.95. (212) 727-0190.

54.

PAIN DOWN THE DRAIN

STEP ONE:
Allow yourself at least 5 minutes for this exercise. Get into the most comfortable position possible and close your eyes. Clear away any extraneous thoughts that might be interfering. For this exercise, you're going to use your imagination as if it were a television set, picturing your body.

STEP TWO:
Imagine you are transparent and filled to the top of your head with green fluid (or any color that represents pain to you). Imagine the liquid beginning to drain out through your fingertips and toes. Picture the level of fluid beginning to drop, from the top of your head, past your eyes, nose, mouth, down through and out your fingertips. Feel the pain and tension draining from your body with the pain liquid. Let the liquid drain down past your back, hips, thighs, knees, legs, into your feet, and out the ends of your toes. (Perform this exercise slowly; don't try to rush.)

Now, picture your body and see if there are any puddles of pain left. If there are, imagine soaking them up with a paper towel.

STEP THREE:
Finish your exercise by using the breathing technique for 30 seconds. Open your eyes, feel refreshed and relaxed.

From *Power Over Your Pain Without Drugs* by Neal Olshan. © 1980. Beaufort Books/SBN Publishing, New York, NY $12.95. (212) 727-0190.

55
PAIN MEDICATION 101

There are several important points to remember about medication and pain control:

- The medication must equal the pain. There are three types of pain: mild, moderate, and severe. And there are three classifications of drugs for mild, moderate, and severe pain. Taking a drug designed for mild pain when you are experiencing severe pain is like using a squirt gun on a house fire. No amount of mild medication will be able to touch the pain. Be honest and specific about the degree of pain you experience. Otherwise, the prescribed drug may be inappropriate.

- Medication must be taken before the pain becomes intense. Many people "tough it out" and wait until the pain gets really bad before taking medication. Once the pain has traveled from the original site through all the nerve receptors in the body and into the brain, it takes a long time for medication to reverse that cycle. For most people, it's best to take medication on a regular schedule (every 3 or 4 hours, for example) around the clock to prevent the pain cycle from starting.

- Morphine is no longer considered a "last effort" drug. The American College of Physicians, the American Medical Association, and the World Health Organization all agree that oral morphine is the drug of choice for chronic, severe pain. It's a myth that morphine use leads to addiction. The chemical make-up of oral morphine closely resembles the body's own pain-killing endorphins. When pain becomes less severe, the person's need for the drug automatically decreases.

- In short, the right drug in the right dose given at the right time relieves 85 to 90 percent of pain. People who are *knowledgeable* about their pain and *assertive enough* to ask for what they need usually achieve an acceptable level of pain control over long periods of time.

From *I Can Cope* by Judith L. Johnson, R.N., Ph.D. and Linda Klein. © 1994. CHRONIMED Publishing, Minneapolis, MN $9.95. (800) 444-5951.

56

BETTER SLEEP

People with painful conditions often find their pain prevents them from having a deep, restful sleep. A solution? Sleep deepens when the body temperature falls. As the temperature rises—generally after five o'clock in the morning—you begin to wake up. Deepen your sleep by taking a 20-minute very hot bath (about 103°) 2 hours before bedtime, then read or relax as the body's internal thermostat pulls your temperature down.

From an interview with Rosalind Cartwright, Ph.D., director of the Sleep Disorders Service and Research Center, Rush-Presbyterian-St. Luke's Medical Center, and author of *Crisis Dreaming,* HarperCollins, New York, NY $20. (212) 207-7000. In *Bottom Line Personal,* 24 issues per year/$49 per year or $4 per issue. (800) 274-5611.

57
PRESSURE POINTS

Consider trying acupressure—an alternative form of massage in which gentle pressure is applied with the thumb and fingers to the traditional acupuncture "pressure points." A physical therapist can tell you more about this form of pain management.

From *Coping with Pain—The Battle Half Won.* The Arthritis Foundation, P.O. Box 19000, Atlanta, GA 30326 Free. (404) 872-7100.

58
MORE GREAT PAINBUSTERS

- Heat is often helpful for chronic pain because it helps muscles to relax. Use a hot shower or bath as your therapy, or soak towels in warm water to which some fresh-grated gingerroot has been added. Wring out and apply hot towels to the area of pain. (Note of caution: People with certain allergies, blood clotting problems, certain types of malignancies, and severe depression should consult a physician before using heat treatment for pain.)

- Try using cold compresses or even ice massage on the area of pain. Acute pain seems to respond generally well to this natural form of anesthetic. (Caution here: Don't overdo your use of ice on the skin, as frostbite could result. Also, those with rheumatoid arthritis or allergies that produce hives are advised against prolonged cold. Some people develop blood clotting abnormalities from exposure to extreme cold.)

- Massage the painful place, or move your hands in a circular motion in the air above the painful area. This massages the "aura" and can be as soothing as direct physical contact.

- Experiment with applying pressure to sensitive areas on your feet and hands, since these may be connection points for pain in other parts of the body.

- Carry on a conversation with your pain, or else write out a dialogue with it in a journal. Ask it why it's here now, what it has to teach you, and how it can be alleviated.

- Place your focus on pleasure. Devise any means available to pleasure yourself.

From *The Fine Art of Recuperation, A Guide to Surviving and Thriving After Illness, Accident or Surgery* by Regina Sara Ryan. © 1991. Jeremy P. Tarcher Publishing/Putnam Publishing Group, Los Angeles, CA $9.95 (presently out of print). For a complete catalog of Jeremy Tarcher titles, including several related to self-help and the healing process, call (213) 935-9980.

59
ADAPTABILITY

If you're feeling truly overwhelmed by pain, this simple formula may help you focus on the positive and cope somewhat better.

A Accept—keep active and occupied.

D Direct yourself outward.

A Aim for reasonable goals and learn to completely relax.

P Pace your activities, staying within your limitations. (It may be necessary to reassess your priorities.)

T Take medications wisely. Be open and reasonable in dealing with your doctors.

Reprinted with permission of CHRONIC PAIN OUTREACH OF GREATER ST. LOUIS, INC. via Lona Polk, Executive Administrator, P.O. Box 31686, Des Peres, MO 63131. (314) 963-3350.

PAIN FIGHTER IN TRAINING

It's possible to train yourself to combat pain. A brief outline of the process involves the following steps:

Pain Diagram — Mentally zero in on the exact area(s) of pain in your body. Think of your body as a diagram that will be used in your mental imagery as a targeting device for your built-in painkillers, endorphins.

Pain Color — A pain color is one that can be used to visibly represent your discomfort. The most popular colors to describe pain appear to be red, black, or dark blue (or purple).

Pain Object(s) — Selecting your pain object or objects is an extremely important aspect of your total pain control imagery program and the development of your personalized pain relief formula. When you combine your pain object with the pain color, you'll have your personalized representation of what pain would look like in your body. Be as graphic and detailed as possible. Once you have combined the pain object and the pain color, you'll have the pain target for your endorphins.

Pain Control Color —The pain control color should be powerful. It's your representation of what color the endorphins (feel-better hormones) are within your body. Some choices for the pain control color have been yellow, light blue, orange, and green.

Pain Control Object(s) — The pain control object or objects will also be part of your personalized representation of the body's built-in painkiller system. The pain object will be attacked by your pain control object. Make sure your pain control object is your own creation; don't rush or take someone else's suggestion. Take all the time you need and make sure your pain control object is a product of your own imagination and thought process.

From *The Scottsdale Pain Relief Program* by Dr. Neal H. Olshan. © 1987. Beaufort Books/SBN Publishing, New York, NY $16.95. (212) 727-0190.

61

SAME STIMULUS, BUT DIFFERENT RESPONSE

Response to pain seems more favorable when the pain is predictable and within a person's control. Patients who are told before surgery about what will happen after surgery need less pain medication and recover more quickly than those not educated before surgery. Greater pain is felt when the cause of your pain is ambiguous and complex. Fear and anxiety fan the flames of pain, especially if the pain is interpreted as being from a life-threatening source.

When your pain is associated with something beneficial, such as in childbirth or winning a game, it's not accompanied by much anxiety and suffering is minimized. There are many stories of injured athletes who finished an event, only to collapse in pain afterward.

Patients who communicate openly with their physicians require less pain medication. This sense of relief seems to come from a reduction in psychological tension.

Pain seems to be more intense when you are alone, at night, or when you have no source of help or nothing to take your mind off it. Pain is worse when the doctor is unavailable, like at night or during the weekend, and when there is less diversions to keep your mind off the pain. Pain may astonishingly improve while you're on the way to see the doctor.

The ability to tolerate pain is *reduced* with high anxiety, depression, an introverted personality, concentrating a lot on bodily functions, and focusing on the internal stimuli from your body. The ability to tolerate pain is *increased* with low anxiety, an extroverted personality, minimal concentration on your bodily functions, and focusing on external stimuli.

Some people tend to increase their pain, while others are able to reduce pain and its effects. Two keys seem to be dealing with anxiety and staying in touch with stimuli from the outside world. Anxiety may be reduced with knowing what the pain means and providing a means of relief, whether it involves heat, traction, bracing, mechanical devices, cold, massage, relaxation techniques, imagery, pain medication, exercise, diversion, family and cultural dynamics, or your own unique personality and belief system.

From *Successful Living with Chronic Illness* by Kathleen Lewis. © 1989. Avery Publishing Group, Garden City Park, NY $10. To order: (404) 491-6850.

62

JUST LOOK INTO MY EYES

Although it's still considered controversial by many physicians, hypnosis, which is actually just a state of highly focused awareness similar to daydreaming, may help take your mind off pain. A psychiatrist or psychologist can help you learn how to use hypnosis techniques.

From *Coping with Pain—The Battle Half Won*. The Arthritis Foundation, P.O. Box 19000, Atlanta, GA 30326 Free. (404) 872-7100.

THE LEANING TOWER OF STRENGTH

Learn to lean on people—not a lot, but just enough to let them know you're there.

CONSIDERING A PAIN SUPPORT GROUP?

A chronic pain outreach program can help you achieve better control over pain by...

- SUPPORTING individuals and families through personal exchanges of coping techniques about day-to-day living;

- EDUCATING families, friends, and the community about chronic pain and treatment resources;

- ADVOCATING for greater awareness and understanding of unmet needs;

- RESEARCHING the causes, treatment, and prevention of chronic pain.

Many pain outreach programs offer regular monthly meetings, a 24-hour a day answering service, a resource library, newsletters and helpful publications, and ongoing educational presentations.

If you're dealing with chronic pain, the most important thing to remember is not to isolate yourself. Get support by contacting the Chronic Pain Outreach group nearest you. To get information on your local chapter, write or call the two national organizations below. They can also assist you with a "starter kit" if you'd like to start your own Chronic Pain Outreach Group.

National Chronic Pain Outreach. 7979 Old Georgetown Rd., Suite 100, Bethesda, MD 20814-2429 Phone (301) 652-4948 or Fax (301) 907-0745.

American Chronic Pain Association, P.O. Box 850, Rocklin, CA 95677. Phone (916) 632-0922.

REDEFINING CONTROL

The unpredictability of chronic pain makes it seem we have lost control of our lives. In addition, the standard we may have set for ourselves in our daily lives may no longer be attainable, causing an even greater sense of helplessness. In reality, however, we are still in control of many areas of our lives. And, by redirecting our standards of achievement to the management of pain, we can experience a high degree of control in that area as well.

From *How to Beat the Chronic Pain Blues* by Sandy Plotz. $3. Reprinted with permission of CHRONIC PAIN OUTREACH OF GREATER ST. LOUIS, INC. via Lona Polk, Executive Administrator. P.O. Box 31686. Des Peres, MO 63131. (314) 963-3350.

12 STEPS TO MORE EFFECTIVE PAIN CONTROL

1. Accept the fact of having pain.

2. Set specific goals for work, hobbies, and social activities toward which you will work.

3. Let yourself get angry with your pain if it seems to be getting the best of you.

4. Take your analgesics on a strict schedule, and then taper off until you're no longer taking any.

5. Get in the best physical shape possible, and keep fit.

6. Learn how to relax, and practice relaxation techniques regularly.

7. Keep yourself busy.

8. Pace your activities.

9. Have family and friends support only your healthy behavior, not your invalidism.

10. Be open and reasonable with your doctor.

11. Practice effective empathy with others having pain problems.

12. Remain hopeful.

From *Mastering Pain* by Dr. Richard A. Sternbach. © 1987. Putnam Publishing Group, New York, NY $4.95. (800) 631-8571.

UNSTRESS FOR SUCCESS

**"Not the whole bed, nurse,
just his mattress."**

67

TRUE ADMISSIONS

One of the most boring (and stressful) parts of a hospital stay occurs right at the beginning—getting admitted. This process can go smoothly, or it can be a nightmare. The purpose of admission is to take care of the paperwork for billing insurers, for billing you, and for the permanent medical record.

On a normal day, the admission process takes about 20 minutes. But if you phone ahead and give your insurance and personal information (in some hospitals they'll even call you) such as birth date and Social Security and insurance card numbers, you can cut it to about 10 minutes.

From "Your Guide to Getting Good Hospital Care" by Tim Friend. © *USA Today,* June 19, 1991. Reprinted with permission. $107 per year for 5 issues per week. (800) 872-0001.

68
TALK IT OUT

Bottling up all the worries and fears you have right now only builds up steam and tension. Someone once said a good friend is worth 100 psychiatrists. Confide in someone you respect and trust—your husband or wife, father or mother, a good friend, your clergyperson, your family physician, a teacher, or a school counselor. Talking about problems won't solve them. But just having the conversation will reduce stress. And then seek professional assistance if necessary. You're worth it!

From *I Can Cope* by Judith L. Johnson, R.N., Ph.D. and Linda Klein. © 1994. CHRONIMED Publishing, Minneapolis, MN $9.95. (800) 444-5951.

YOU ARE NOT ALONE

Your normal life may have turned upside down or inside out by this health crisis. The grief or panic that accompanies such a major upheaval may leave you feeling quite insecure or wondering if you are losing it or going crazy. But these reactions are normal.

The first prescription for riding the sometimes frightening or confusing emotional waves that accompany a health crisis is to recognize that you're not alone in what you're going through. Others have felt this way too, and often. And while this may not relieve your pain, it may help to relieve some of your anxiety about it. Truly, nobody else has ever experienced crisis in exactly the same way you have. Yet the reports of many recuperating people about what they felt, what they feared, and what surprised them are remarkably similar despite age differences or types of illness.

From *The Fine Art of Recuperation, A Guide to Surviving and Thriving After Illness, Accident or Surgery* by Regina Sara Ryan. © 1991. Jeremy P. Tarcher Publishing/Putnam Publishing Group, Los Angeles, CA $9.95 (presently out of print). For a complete catalog of Jeremy Tarcher titles, including several related to self-help and the healing process, call (213) 935-9980.

70
WARMING TREND

Here's a pleasant relaxation exercise to try when you're uncomfortable, stressed, or in pain:

Close your eyes.

Inhale deeply through your nose.

Hold your breath for a silent count of six.

Exhale slowly through your mouth.

Repeat this rhythmic breathing five times.

With your eyes still closed, start at the top of your head and imagine as if someone had just begun to pour pleasantly warm water on your hair and the warmth was beginning to gently flow down your body. Picture in your mind's eye (mental imagery) the warm liquid slowly moving down your body and relaxing all the muscles it passes over.

Stop at any muscles that seem tense or tight or where you're having any pain.

Don't rush; take your time.

Keep your breathing calm and regular.

When you reach your feet, there will be a general sensation of heaviness in the body, and you may feel some warmth in your arms and legs.

Repeat the breathing part of the formula five more times, silently counting to six while you hold your breath and then exhale slowly through your mouth.

Take one deep breath, and let it out in a regular manner. Open your eyes, gently stretch your arms and legs, and get up slowly.

It's important to note that you should never stand up quickly or jump up following this exercise since you might become faint or dizzy and fall.

From *The Scottsdale Pain Relief Program* by Dr. Neal H. Olshan. © 1987. Beaufort Books/SBN Publishing, New York, NY $16.95. (212) 727-0190.

71
HOLIDAYS WHEN YOU'RE RECUPERATING

The heightened emotions of the holidays may be seen in the extremes of "highs" and "lows"—happiness and depression. Blessings and losses are both magnified. We are thankful for the blessings of love and remembrance. We also become sad as we are vividly reminded of losses—health, goals, ambitions, functions—maybe even loved ones or changed relationships. It can be a sober time for reflection. You might take some time to think about where your life is and what is really important.

Try not to spend your holidays completely alone if you can help it. It's very important to share them with someone else. Find someone to spend a little time with, even if it's just on the phone. Whenever possible, capture the message of the music of the season. Whole meals can be catered, if necessary. Pre-cooked turkeys and hams can be purchased. Find your own unique way to reach out to others, staying within your limits. Be good to yourself on special days and find ways to celebrate holidays as well as every other day of the year.

From *Successful Living with Chronic Illness* by Kathleen Lewis. © 1989. Avery Publishing Group, Garden City Park, NY $10. To order: (404) 491-6850.

72
CLASSIC REMEDIES

These music selections were chosen for their overall life-supporting quality. Rather than causing you to separate or dissociate from your body, these musical pieces will each encourage an alignment within you, helping you to harmonize yourself with the natural healing rhythm of your body, and the real, healing energies of the earth. All this music is vitalizing. It contains struggle at times, but is always victorious:

Bach, *Double Concerto or Violin Concertos* 1 and 2. Stimulates joy, serenity, and a sense of radiance.

Bach, *Brandenburg Concertos.* Many excellent recordings. Tremendous variety. Experience a full range of feelings.

Mozart, *Violin Concertos* 3 and 5. Inspires magic, joy, and a sense of delight.

Pachelbel's Canon/Baroque Favorites. Soothing, full, rich, and life-supporting.

Chopin, *Nocturnes.* Restful, dreamy, and peaceful.

Mahler, *Symphony no.* 4. Full of delightful, life-giving sounds.

Beethoven, *Symphony no.* 6 (the *Pastoral*). Inspires happiness and contentment.

Dvorák, *Cello Concerto,* and Tchiakovsky, *Rococo Variations.* Full of richness, earthiness, and warmth.

Mendelssohn, *Violin Concertos*, and Tchiakovsky, *Violin Concertos.* Heart-filling, vibrant, and passionate.

From *The Fine Art of Recuperation, A Guide to Surviving and Thriving After Illness, Accident or Surgery* by Regina Sara Ryan. © 1991. Jeremy P. Tarcher Publishing/Putnam Publishing Group, Los Angeles, CA $9.95 (presently out of print). For a complete catalog of Jeremy Tarcher titles, including several related to self-help and the healing process, call (213) 935-9980.

73

WHY A GOOD CRY IS A GOOD THING

Whether you're a man or a woman, this advice can come in handy. What do you do if you've identified the reason for the bad feelings, communicated with others about them, sought information, tried solutions—and nothing helps? This is the time for a good cry. Give in, beat the pillow, throw a few items at the walls (assuming you're at home), and get that tension out of your system. We recommend throwing a light object such as a Nerf ball, since it will give your arm muscles some exercise and won't damage walls or shatter. It may seem absurd to picture yourself throwing sponge balls and sobbing (especially if you're the type of man who's unaccustomed to crying), but nature gave us all the ability to cry for sound reasons. A good cry relieves stress and allows you to gather your coping skills once again.

From *Pregnancy Bedrest: A Guide for the Pregnant Woman and Her Family* by Susan H. Johnston, M.S.W. and Deborah A. Kraut, M.I.L.R. © 1990. Henry Holt, New York, NY $14.95. (212) 886-9200.

DIVE INTO THE POOL OF FORGIVENESS

1. Close your eyes and begin to feel a sense of inner peace and stillness.

2. Take a few deep breaths. As you breathe out, imagine you are breathing out all tensions and past thoughts. Breathe as deeply as you can.

3. As you breathe in, tell yourself you are breathing in peace and stillness. Continue to breathe in peace and breathe out negativity.

4. Imagine that in front of you is a pool of pure light, perhaps a shaft of sunlight.

5. As you imagine the pool, start to think of some of the things you would like to let go. They may be things about yourself or someone else.

6. Start to let go of these thoughts and feelings, releasing them into the pool. Breathe them out.

7. Say them out loud as you release each one, but as you let go, use the words "I LOVE . . . "
   (For example, "I love my resentments about . . ." "I love my fear." "I love my anger toward my spouse." "I love my thoughts." "I love my body," etc.)

8. When you feel ready to move on, continue to let go aloud, but this time use the words, "I FORGIVE . . . "
   (For example, "I forgive myself for all the times I've hurt myself." "I forgive myself for being afraid." "I forgive my spouse for not loving me in the way I needed." "I forgive myself for being overcritical," etc.)

9. Now open your eyes, and in the same spirit of letting go, say "I'M WILLING TO RECEIVE . . . "
   (For example, "I'm willing to receive all the love and support I need." "I'm willing to receive my spouse the way he or she is." "I'm willing to receive peace of mind," etc.)

From *Coping with Cancer; Making Sense of It All* by Rachael Clyne. © 1989 Thorsons Publishing Group/HarperCollins Publishing, Wellingborough, England and New York, NY (212) 207-7000.

75
24-HOUR STRESS SOOTHER

A round-the-clock telephone service of New York's Lenox Hill Hospital offers recorded stress-reducing messages. Call the hospital's Tel-Med service at (212) 434-3200 and select the stress-reduction information tape.

76
UNPACE YOURSELF

Learn to pace yourself. Whether you're at home or in the hospital, schedule small rest periods between tasks throughout the day. If necessary, use a timer. Cut a particularly difficult task into small, manageable parts over several days. And, if an especially busy day is scheduled, plan to spend the next one resting. Though it sounds like time wasted, pacing will, in the long run SAVE time as well as energy and give you the best results for your efforts.

From *How to Beat the Chronic Pain Blues* by Sandy Plotz. $3. Reprinted with permission of CHRONIC PAIN OUTREACH OF GREATER ST. LOUIS, INC., via Lona Polk, Executive Administrator, P.O. Box 31686, Des Peres, MO 63131. (314) 963-3350.

77

STRESS BUSTING WITH SOOTHING SOUNDS

Check your local record store for the Environments series or Solitude series recordings. You can order them yourself by calling Backroads Distributors at (800) 825-4848. For a catalog, write Backroads, 417 Tamal Plaza, Corte Madera, CA 94925.

From *The Fine Art of Recuperation, A Guide to Surviving and Thriving After Illness, Accident or Surgery* by Regina Sara Ryan. © 1991. Jeremy P. Tarcher Publishing/Putnam Publishing Group, Los Angeles, CA $9.95 (presently out of print). For a complete catalog of Jeremy Tarcher titles, including several related to self-help and the healing process, call (213) 935-9980.

78

SLEEP EASY

Sleep can be one of the most important healing forces in a person's life. To assure you get adequate rest, try not to take your worries to bed with you. If you're plagued by insomnia, remember what Dr. David Viscott says in his book *A Natural Sleep*— "you can't solve all your problems at once."

If you still can't sleep, you may also want to take the extra step of writing down all your problems and some possible solutions for each one. Your plan of action will help you realize you're not as helpless as you thought and that you don't have to think about your worries all the time.

79

THREE PATHS THROUGH THE FOREST

A person can react in three different ways to a chronic illness. The first is to give up and forgo any treatment. The second is to deny the diagnosis is true, which leads to despair because you get nowhere. The third road is to get active in your own behalf and take responsibility for your well-being and your goals for the future.

From *Successful Living with Chronic Illness* by Kathleen Lewis. © 1989. Avery Publishing Group, Garden City Park, NY $10. To order: (404) 491-6850.

PERFECT TIMING

Recuperation is the "perfect" opportunity to overcome a tendency for perfectionism. Learning to laugh at mistakes and enjoy being human is one of the keys to conquering anxiety. The following approaches are proven methods for eliminating perfectionistic tendencies and replacing them with positive opposites.

The first step is to memorize ideas that can be used to challenge the mistaken concept that perfection is possible and desirable. Most people find the following ideas effective:

- Perfection is, by definition, a goal that is impossible to reach.

- The idea of perfection is an abstract concept that only exists in theory.

- There is always some imperfection, some improvement that can be made in everything you see and do.

- Because we live in an imperfect world, a person who strives for perfection is guaranteed failure.

Underlying perfectionistic behavior is a search for belonging and significance. People with perfectionistic tendencies often base their behavior on the mistaken idea that worth is determined by achievement. The combination of this mistaken idea and perfectionistic tendencies creates a no-win situation in which you feel worthwhile only when you achieve, but your achievements always fall short of your perfectionistic standards. The result is a feeling that you never do enough and are always falling short of what is required.

Many people have found the following ideas enable them to successfully challenge the mistaken idea that worth is determined by achievement:

- Your value as a person is entirely separate from the value of the activities you do. Equating worth with achievement is an arbitrary value system for which there is no objective support. Technically you are only a human being who does various activities. You are not these activities. While your activities may or may not be valuable, they do not add or subtract from your value as a person.

- People usually achieve more when achievement is the result of enjoying an activity rather than the result of being sought as a source of self-worth and self-esteem.

- Overconcern with achievement creates anxiety that interferes with your ability to achieve.

- A person can be average and still be effective and enjoy life. In fact, many very happy and successful people have below average talent and ability.

- When people look back on their lives, they usually find the satisfaction they received from how they lived was far more important than what they did.

- As far as healthy, satisfying, long-term relationships are concerned, who you are as a person is far more important than what you achieve.

From *Anxiety, Phobias, and Panic: Taking Charge & Conquering Fear* by Reneau Z. Peurifoy, M.A., M.F.C.C. © 1992. Lifeskills, P.O. Box 7915, Citrus Heights, CA 95621 $12.95. (916) 723-7517.

81
RELAXING TO A BEAT

For a high-tech way to de-stress, consider the Master Mind, a computer-directed audiovisual system that uses rhythmic pulsing light and sound to guide your mind into a state of deep relaxation. A software system contained within the Master Mind's hand-held control unit directs 12 different preset programs with a choice of four sounds that match actual patterns of brainwave activity. Once a program is chosen, a series of soothing lights seen through closed eyes behind dark glasses, synchronizes in the user's mind with custom-designed sounds channeled into the headset. Mentally harmonizing with the frequencies of these stimuli, the user (hopefully) moves into a state of deep relaxation and heightened creativity normally experienced while dreaming. Programs vary from 15 to 60 minutes. Runs on a 9-volt battery, which is included. $199.95 from Hammacher Schlemmer, (800) 543-3366. Or write the Hammacher Schlemmer Operations Center, 2515 E. 43rd St., P.O. Box 182256, Chattanooga, TN 37422.

82
KOOSHY KOOSHY KOO

My favorite personal stress-buster is a Koosh ball, the snuggly porcupine-like ball with soft rubbery bristles that makes it hard to put down. Throw it, roll it, or just be comforted by it. It is available in large or small sizes or in animal shapes at most toy stores.

83

SLOW MO PRO

A pleasant way to de-stress at home or the hospital is to watch the colorful glass floats rising and falling inside a 16-1/2" replica of Galileo's famous "Termometro Lento" (Slow Thermometer). As the room gets cooler, the globes rise. As it warms up, they fall. In blue or burgundy. $175 from Attitudes, (800) 525-2468, 24 hours a day. Or write to: Attitudes, P.O. Box 61148, Sunnyvale, CA 94088-1148.

84

GREAT TIMING

There's no need to apologize for filling time or (heaven help us!) even wasting time when in bed. The only criterion for what you do with your time is whether it supports you in feeling good about yourself, which means it will assist your healing. Consider these hints as you plan your time:

- Generally, it's not advisable to try heavy reading while you're still in the hospital. Keep the world's problems off your back for as long as you can. Even reading the newspaper or watching the TV news may expose you to more bad news than you want. Experiment with remaining uninformed for a few days at a time, and learn what that does for your spirits. When "wounded" in any way, you're more susceptible to depressing news than you would be if you were stronger.

- Your energy will last better if you vary your activities and take frequent time-outs. Take 5-minute stretch breaks every hour. Take 5-minute breathing times, when you do nothing else. Take five to gaze out the window and enjoy the sky. Take five to listen to some favorite music or to make yourself a special cup of tea. Make a 5-minute phone call—to encourage someone else, to catch up on news, to share your concerns. Take 5 minutes to pray. Take 5 minutes to practice smiling or to laugh or hum. Take 5 minutes to massage your hands or feet or face. Take a 5-minute nap.

- Give yourself permission to do nothing and to enjoy it. The world would be a much better place if more people did nothing now and then, don't you agree? Just think of all the messes that might never have been made, to say nothing of wars. Doing nothing also conserves energy. It doesn't cost anything. It's even nonfattening.

From *The Fine Art of Recuperation, A Guide to Surviving and Thriving After Illness, Accident or Surgery* by Regina Sara Ryan. © 1991. Jeremy P. Tarcher Publishing/Putnam Publishing Group, Los Angeles, CA $9.95 (presently out of print). For a complete catalog of Jeremy Tarcher titles, including several related to self-help and the healing process, call (213) 935-9980.

VISITING OURS

"Bob, these are doctors Burton, Kane, and
Roycefield...they'll be assisting me with your
health insurance forms."

85
JUST VISITING

In most hospitals visiting hours are fairly generous (except in intensive care units, where limits generally make sense). However, if you're scared, lonely, or worried about tomorrow's procedure, then it's your right as a patient and as a fragile human being to have your visitor or visitors stay with you past visiting hours. Perhaps you need your visitor to spend the night nearby. If the nurse tries to send the visitor away, stand your ground. Ask to see the head nurse. If you're not satisfied, demand to see the patient's representative or the hospital administrator, no matter what time it is. If you must, call your doctor at home. You can have somebody there with you past hours if you want. On the other hand, if you do not want visitors, don't have them. Politely ask the staff to arrange this.

From *Take This Book to the Hospital With You* by Charles B. Inlander and Ed Weiner. © 1991. Pantheon Books/Random House, New York, NY by People's Medical Society $14.95. (800) 733-3000.

TOUGH TOPICS

If you're having trouble talking about your illness or injury with people close to you, here are some opening statements for initiating discussion of uncomfortable thoughts and feelings adapted from *The Road Back to Health,* by Neil A. Fiore, Ph.D.

- I feel like my illness/injury made us strangers, and I'm becoming isolated and alienated from you. Right now we're both suffering privately. Is there anything I can do to help you through this time?

- We've been dancing around the issue of my condition a lot lately. Can't we find a way to really talk?

- It's hard for me to tell you my feelings about my illness/injury. And I'm afraid it will upset you if I bring it up.

From *I Can Cope* by Judith L. Johnson, R.N., Ph.D. and Linda Klein © 1994. CHRONIMED Publishing, Minneapolis, MN $9.95. (800) 444-5951.

87
HEALING HUGS

Sometimes a genuine hug is all you need to make your day. Yet many folks don't give themselves permission to hug or hold in a way that really allows for a merging of life-energy. A healing hug is one that allows you to relax into another's arms, if only for a few seconds, to feel the tangible, physical support of another human being. You might suggest that your friend or care giver give you a "breakfast hug," my term for a gentle but complete embrace in which one partner acts as the warm toast, the other partner as the butter. Maintain the contact until both of you agree the butter is completely melted, absorbed into the toast.

From *The Fine Art of Recuperation, A Guide to Surviving and Thriving After Illness, Accident or Surgery* by Regina Sara Ryan. © 1991. Jeremy P. Tarcher Publishing/Putnam Publishing Group, Los Angeles, CA $9.95 (presently out of print). For a complete catalog of Jeremy Tarcher titles, including several related to self-help and the healing process, call (213) 935-9980.

88
COUNT YOUR SUPPORTERS

It can be very helpful to take a few minutes to remember the people who could assist you now or at some later time. This exercise can help:

- Divide a piece of paper into two columns. On the top of the left-hand column, write Places I Go. On the top of the right-hand column, write People I Meet.

Start by listing all the places you go to or went to regularly before your accident or illness. Include evening places as well as daytime places, places you go to regularly once a month, like a meeting or your church or social group, and even places you go to regularly, but infrequently, as with that annual visit you make to see your childhood friend.

On the right side of the chart, list the people you regularly see or meet at the places you have indicated.

- Now take a fresh sheet to continue your list of contacts. Write the name of anyone you know who meets the following criteria. Consult the list you just made for additional names.

> trustworthy with money
> very good listener
> understanding and compassionate
> seems to enjoy helping others
> easy to be with
> makes me laugh
> very bright about practical matters
> offered help if I ever needed it

- Just in case you've forgotten someone obvious, make a list of friends, colleagues at work, and relatives.

- Now that you've completed these memory-jogging lists, consider who may be available to you for ongoing or occasional support. Put a check or asterisk next to the names of those whom you would be comfortable either sharing with or asking for some help. Double the symbol for those you feel very comfortable about, and you'll have your first-string support list.

- Now take a new sheet of paper and label it My Best Possible Supporters. Write the name of your first-string team, one name to a line. Follow with the list of your single-symbol supporters. You now have identified your best potential sources of support, conversation, companionship, and assistance.

From *The Fine Art of Recuperation, A Guide to Surviving and Thriving After Illness, Accident or Surgery* by Regina Sara Ryan. © 1991. Jeremy P. Tarcher Publishing/Putnam Publishing Group, Los Angeles, CA $9.95 (presently out of print). For a complete catalog of Jeremy Tarcher titles, including several related to self-help and the healing process, call (213) 935-9980.

89

HELPING HANDS

If friends offer to help you, don't be shy about telling them the things that would make you feel better right now. If you can't think of anything, you might ask them to bring over dinner the first night you're home from the hospital.

From Ellen Bern and Barry Mizes, St. Louis, MO.

90

PLEASE TOUCH

Massage will relieve tension and help to alleviate pain and stiffness in your body. It stimulates blood flow and electrical energy in your nervous system to wake up the parts of you that are going to sleep. It will also help break up the emotional blockages caused by your trauma. And best of all, it just feels good.

You don't need a professional to get the nurturing and healing benefits of massage. If you're lucky enough to have a friend or care giver willing to give you a massage—a back or foot rub, a scalp massage, a facial, or more—speak up. Tell your friend what feels good. Keep in mind that you are doing your visitors a favor by your specific request.

From *The Fine Art of Recuperation, A Guide to Surviving and Thriving After Illness, Accident or Surgery* by Regina Sara Ryan. © 1991. Jeremy P. Tarcher Publishing/Putnam Publishing Group, Los Angeles, CA $9.95 (presently out of print). For a complete catalog of Jeremy Tarcher titles, including several related to self-help and the healing process, call (213) 935-9980.

91

CONNECTING TO THE OUTSIDE WORLD

Ask your visitors to bring a part of life into the hospital: flowers, magazines and books, familiar foods, appealing objects. Ask them to discuss the things you have in common: music, television shows, politics or news, or affairs of the heart, business or family.

From *You Can Make It Back: Coping with Serious Illness* by Paul M. Levitt and Elissa S. Guralnick. © 1985. Facts on File Publications, New York, NY $16.95. Currently out of print but still available in many libraries. (212) 683-2244.

HOW TO RELAX IN SPITE OF YOURSELF

"How's he sleeping at night?"

HEADACHE HELPER

Here's a quick relaxation exercise when you have a headache or feel a lot of tension in your face:

- Squeeze your eyes shut for 7 seconds

- Let your lids go limp

- Squeeze your eyes together half as tightly as before

- Relax

- Squeeze again, half as tightly as the last time

- Relax

- Repeat, each time halving the muscle tension

- Repeat this halving exercise until your entire forehead feels free of tension and stressful energy.

From an interview of Keith Sedlacek, author of *The Sedlacek Technique.* $17.95. Also available: two audio tapes of accompanying relaxation exercises for $14.95. (212) 512-2000. Reprinted with permission from *Bottom Line Personal,* 330 W. 42nd St., New York, NY 10036. 24 issues per year/$49 per year or $4 per issue. (800) 274-5611.

RELAX YOUR MIND AND FEEL YOUR BODY FOLLOW

It can be difficult to relax when your mind and body are both clamoring for your attention with negative messages. One way to get around this is to concentrate on something that is neutral—neither good nor bad. This can help to clear the mind of the concerns of the moment, freeing it for more relaxing activity.

For some people, there's a more directed approach to relaxation. Instead of trying not to think about anything, you can imagine how you will feel when you are relaxed. Tension has some very specific effects on your body—so the key is to imagine the opposite effect. For example, when people get stressed, extremities like hands and feet become cooler as the body redirects blood away from those areas. So imagine that your hands and feet are nice and warm. Other signs of relaxation are a cool forehead, relaxed jaw, unclenched hands, slow deep breathing, and a steady heartbeat.

Write a few short sentences of how you will feel when you are relaxed. Simple sentences like "my hands are warm" are best. If you can, find some quiet time and repeat your relaxation list slowly 10 times.

From *Coping With Pain: Focus on Cancer.* Vol. 1, No. 3, Spring 1991. The KSF Group, 630 Ninth Avenue, Suite 901, New York, NY 10036. (212) 582-5600.

94

BREATHING EASY

Counting backward is a common relaxation technique. It's found on cassette tapes designed to produce a relaxation response and taught by therapists. Breath counting is an effective adaptation of this approach for a person working on his or her own.

1. Pick a time and place where you won't be disturbed and lie or sit in a comfortable position. If you're in a hospital bed, try to position the bed at the most comfortable angle or ask a nurse to do this for you.

2. Close your eyes and begin counting backward from 50. Time each count in the following manner to match your breathing. After you exhale, notice that you don't have to breathe in again immediately and can rest comfortably for a few seconds. For some people, this may only be one or two seconds. For others it may be as long as 20 seconds. Count during this peaceful time when the lungs have paused and the body is still. Count one number for each cycle of breathing in and out.

As you practice breath counting, you may occasionally lose track of the number you are counting. This is normal. When this occurs, simply resume counting from the last number you remember. If it's 37, resume your count with 36. To spend more time on this exercise, start counting at a higher number such as 75 or 100. One advantage to this method is that, with experience, you can estimate how long it will take to relax.

3. After completing your countdown, you can either return to your normal alert state or spend additional time developing your relaxation response by switching to another method.

From *Anxiety, Phobias and Panic: Taking Charge & Conquering Fear* by Reneau Z. Peurifoy, M.A., M.F.C.C. © 1992. Lifeskills, P.O. Box 7915, Citrus Heights, CA 95621. $12.95 (916) 723-7517.

95

WORTHY RELAXATION CASSETTES

Exercises to guide you in the healing process are available from Source Cassettes, P.O. Box W., Stanford, CA 94309. To order a tape or a catalog, call (800) 52-TAPES. The following tapes are composed and narrated by Emmett Miller, M.D.

Letting Go of Stress. Learn a logical progression from simple to sophisticated techniques for stress management. Four different methods for achieving deep relaxation. (Tape #23)

Healing Journey. Learn techniques for active participation in your body's healing process. Valuable for acute or chronic conditions. (Tape #16)

Successful Surgery and Recovery. Condition the mind and body to achieve maximum benefit and speedy recovery from surgery. Techniques to minimize anesthesia, postoperative swellings, pain, bleeding, and infection. (Tape #203)

Change the Channel on Pain. Tune out pain and tune in relief. People with occasional or chronic pain can learn to "change the channel." (Tape #46)

SKY WATCHING

If you're close to a window, or can go outdoors, use the day or night sky as a source of meditation. Just look. Watch. Breathe. Observe where your thoughts take you. Don't restrict your thoughts. Give them the whole sky to play in.

97

BREATHING LIGHTLY

This exercise will help you relax by "directing" your inhaled air to any part of your body that is particularly tense, such as the shoulders.

1. Sit or lie in a comfortable position. Close your eyes.

2. Breathe in. Imagine you are sending the inhaled air directly to your shoulders (or whatever part needs relaxing).

3. Imagine seeing a faint light or tiny candle flame in the center of the tense body part.

4. As you inhale, "feed" that light or flame with your breath, and watch it as it grows brighter and then expands. You may notice a pleasant warmth in the area of your focus.

5. Make the connection in your mind between the growth of this light and the relaxation of your tension. As the light increases in size and intensity, your tension is diminished.

6. Keep breathing until the light fills your whole body, and then watch as it penetrates your skin from the inside out and forms a flow or aura around the outside of your body.

7. Rest and breathe normally in the aura.

8. After a few minutes, complete this exercise by stretching your fingers and toes and hands and feet. Stretch your neck, face, and whatever else wants to move. Slowly open your eyes.

From *The Fine Art of Recuperation, A Guide to Surviving and Thriving After Illness, Accident or Surgery* by Regina Sara Ryan. © 1991. Jeremy P. Tarcher Publishing/Putnam Publishing Group, Los Angeles, CA $9.95 (presently out of print). For a complete catalog of Jeremy Tarcher titles, including several related to self-help and the healing process, call (213) 935-9980.

OUCH, MY ACHING HEAD!

Here's a quick way to relieve a headache and sinus congestion:

- With your thumbs, apply pressure to the inside eye socket, at the bridge of the nose.

- With the middle finger, apply pressure to the sides of the nose just under the bridge. Find the most sensitive spot. This may stop a sneezing fit or clear up congested nasal passages.

From *The Fine Art of Recuperation, A Guide to Surviving and Thriving After Illness, Accident or Surgery* by Regina Sara Ryan. © 1991. Jeremy P. Tarcher Publishing/Putnam Publishing Group, Los Angeles, CA $9.95 (presently out of print). For a complete catalog of Jeremy Tarcher titles, including several related to self-help and the healing process, call (213) 935-9980.

PALM BALM

This simple relaxation technique uses breathing, visualizing, and blocking sensory stimulation to the eyes.

1. Rub your palms together to warm them.

2. Place one cupped palm over each eye, the fingers of one hand crossing the fingers of the other hand on your forehead.

3. Keep your eyes open. Arrange your palms so no light can be seen.

4. Breathe softly and deeply for eight breaths, feeling warmth rising in your arms and hands, and bathing your eyes.

5. At the same time, imagine a happy and peaceful scene from your past.

6. After the eight breaths, remove your hands from your eyes and look softly around the room.

From *The Fine Art of Recuperation, A Guide to Surviving and Thriving After Illness, Accident or Surgery* by Regina Sara Ryan. © 1991. Jeremy P. Tarcher Publishing/Putnam Publishing Group, Los Angeles, CA $9.95 (presently out of print). For a complete catalog of Jeremy Tarcher titles, including several related to self-help and the healing process, call (213) 935-9980.

100
VISIBLY RELAXING

Focus your eyes on the most soothing sight near you and keep them there. Breathe deeply and don't stop. Mentally repeat: "1,000; 2,000; 3,000; 4,000" as you inhale through your nose. Exhale from your mouth, mentally counting: "1,000; 2,000; 3,000; 4,000." Breathe this way for a full 5 minutes.

Now tense every muscle in your body as tightly as you can. Tense your face; clench your fists and toes, if possible. Hold this for a count of ten. Then slowly release this tension and breathe deeply. Stop thinking and take a rest.

Finally, make a sound such as "ba" or "da" as loudly as you can. Feel the reverberation of the sounds in your body. Keep making the sound until you feel relaxed. Then repeat this phrase to yourself: "I am here, I'm alive, I can cope, I survive."

From *The Fine Art of Recuperation, A Guide to Surviving and Thriving After Illness, Accident or Surgery* by Regina Sara Ryan. © 1991. Jeremy P. Tarcher Publishing/Putnam Publishing Group, Los Angeles, CA $9.95 (presently out of print). For a complete catalog of Jeremy Tarcher titles, including several related to self-help and the healing process, call (213) 935-9980.

DEVELOPING A GREAT IMAGE

**"I have to run some tests to see what tests we
should run on you."**

101
VISUAL TOOLS

Visualization can be an effective healing tool in dealing with illness or injury.

Example: Imagine your injury or disease as an army of enemy invaders, and the immune system as a good army destroying the invading forces.

But warlike images are only helpful to people comfortable with military themes. For others, violent imagery may work against healing by equating illness with violence and slaughter. As an alternative, focus on *fixing* rather than *killing*.

Example: Think of your immune system as a gardening crew pulling up weeds...or a road crew fixing potholes...or a piano tuner restoring harmony to an out-of-tune instrument.

From an interview with linguist Suzette Haden Elgin, Ph.D., author of *Staying Well with the Gentle Art of Verbal Self Defense.* ©1990. Prentice Hall Business and Professional Publishing, Englewood Cliffs, NJ $12.95. (201) 592-2000. Reprinted with permission from *Bottom Line Personal,* 330 W, 42nd St., New York, NY 10036. 24 issues per year/$49 per year or $4 per issue. (800) 274-5611.

102
DAYDREAM BELIEVER

Close your eyes and imagine a favorite street, restaurant, movie theater, department store, or park. Think about what you would do in each place. Plan how to get there, what you would wear, and imagine the sounds of each place. Daydreaming is total concentration and a way to temporarily experience being out of bed.

From *Pregnancy Bedrest: A Guide for the Pregnant Woman and Her Family* by Susan H. Johnston, M.S.W. and Deborah A. Kraut, M.I.L.R. © 1990. Henry Holt, New York, NY $14.95. (212) 886-9200.

103
MORE PLEASANT IMAGES

The following four suggestions from the Arthritis Foundation use imagery, or "mental pictures," to help you relax.

- Light a candle and focus your attention on the flame for a few minutes. Then close your eyes and watch the image of the flame for a minute or two.

- Imagine a white cloud floating toward you. It wraps itself around your pain and stress. Then a breeze comes. It blows away the cloud, taking your pain and stress with it.

- Think about a place you've been where you once felt pleasure and comfort. Imagine as much detail as possible—how it looks, smells, sounds, and feels. Recapture the positive feelings you had then and keep them in your mind. Don't make any room for negative thoughts, stress, or pain.

- Imagine that you've put all your concerns, worries, and pain in a helium-filled balloon. Now let go of the balloon and watch it float away.

104
MIND SAILING

Imagine yourself lying back in a small boat. You have thick, soft cushions tucked under you and around you. You feel comfortable and safe. Your boat is floating down a narrow channel. The sun is filtering through the leaves of oak trees that arch above you. You see the shadows of the leaves flickering on your body.

Underneath you, you feel the gentle rocking of the boat as you float with the current. Water laps softly against the sides of your boat. It's early summer; so it's warm but not sticky or humid. You float downstream. Notice the forest smells and the smells of the waterway. Let all your sensors investigate the world around you.

Look over the side of the boat. See the fish swimming in the stream. Notice their color and shapes as they dart around and under the boat. They look as if they're being reflected in a fun house mirror, distorted by the moving water. Let your hand trail in the stream. Feel the refreshing coolness of the water.

Splash some water on your face. Look around at the banks of the stream. What do you see? Try to remember everything. Look up at the sky. Be aware of everything around you. Feel content and serene as you drift.

You're coming to a tunnel now, but you've been through this tunnel before, so you know what to expect. Darkness, then escape. A good place for shade when it's hot. As you float into the tunnel, you can't see anything except the sunlight sparkling on the water at the other end. Your boat is drifting slowly into the darkness, and your mind wanders. Where does it go? It's always moving, into the past, back into the present, probing into the future. Linger in the tunnel, dream in the tunnel, for as long as you want.

As you come out of the tunnel, feel yourself being covered by golden sunshine. The sunlight wraps itself around you and brings you energy and makes you smile. You glide out of the tunnel and come to a lake.

You float onto the lake. A cool breeze sweeps across your body. The lake is tranquil. Nearly silent. Feel the quiet.

Be aware of everything: the gentle motion of the boat, the warmth of the sun, the fragrances (there's lavender growing nearby), the sounds of just drifting along. Let yourself feel these sensations.

You're floating on the lake, your little boat circling like a satellite, not going anywhere else. This lake is where you want to be.

Come back from this exercise slowly. Reacquaint yourself with where you really are sitting. Open your eyes and look around the room.

From *You Can Relieve Pain: How Guided Imagery Can Help You Reduce Pain or Eliminate It Altogether* by Ken Dachman and John Lyons. © 1990. HarperCollins, New York, NY $18.95. (212) 207-7000.

105

FOLLOW THE BOUNCING BALL

Close your eyes and relax. Think of a red ball, floating in a blue sky. Change the color of the ball. Change it to orange and then to yellow. Move the ball from left to right, up and down; move the ball from side to side, back and forth. Bounce the ball across the bright blue sky.

Bring the ball closer to you. Then send it spinning away toward the horizon. Make the ball fly so far away you can't see it anymore. Then make it fly back toward you.

Make the ball turn into a balloon, then into a kite. Change the kite into a bird, flying around you until you change it into a ball again. Now, give up control of the image. Let your mind take the ball and do whatever it wants to with it.

Take control of the ball again. Bounce the ball through the bright sky. When you're ready to stop, open your eyes and restart your conscious mind.

From *You Can Relieve Pain: How Guided Imagery Can Help You Reduce Pain or Eliminate It Altogether* by Ken Dachman and John Lyons. © 1990. HarperCollins, New York, NY $18.95. (212) 207-7000.

106
CONNECTING THE DOTS

Relax and close your eyes. You're surrounded by blackness, swallowed by peaceful darkness. Imagine a bright dot of red light far in the distance. Make the dot grow larger and larger as it comes slowly toward you. Here it comes, closer and closer.

Before the red light reaches you, it begins to pale, fading gradually from scarlet to rose, then pink, then nearly white, until it disappears altogether.

Go over this process again and again, slowly, until you can imagine the dot, it's approach, and color change, as if it were right there in front of you.

Off in the black distance, another bright dot of light appears. This one is orange. Think of the orange light moving closer and closer, expanding as it floats toward you. Then the bright orange glow begins to fade, growing pale and softer until it vaporizes, becoming a misty cloud before it disappears.

In the darkness, you see a pinpoint of bright yellow light, far away like a miniature sun. It comes toward you, growing larger and brighter, becoming a warm golden circle. Bask in the brightness and warmth of the light. Then the yellow begins to fade, first flaxen, then paler and paler, until the light disappears.

There's a clear green dot of light in the darkness, bright and clear like an emerald. Watch it move closer and closer. The clear green light expands until it envelops you in its waves of green. Then watch the green light get paler and softer as it slowly fades and disappears.

You see a soft pale dot of blue light in the distance. Watch this gentle light as it floats clear, a bubble of light, growing large enough to surround and embrace your entire body. The blue light lifts you gently into the air. It's pale color changes as you rise, and you find yourself floating on a cloud of white and luminous light, like the clouds you see from an airplane window.

Feel yourself drifting up into the sky. Look at other clouds as you float by. The clouds are a tranquil place to be, floating peacefully above the earth.

Float for as long as you like. When it's time to come back, return slowly and gently. Drift back into the darkness and stand on your feet again, back on the firm ground. Take a deep breath; let the air fill your lungs.

From *You Can Relieve Pain: How Guided Imagery Can Help You Reduce Pain or Eliminate It Altogether* by Ken Dachman and John Lyons. © 1990. HarperCollins, New York, NY $18.95. (212) 207-7000.

107

THE FLIP SIDE OF PAIN

This visualization exercise is designed to help you "flip" the negative images you associate with your pain, tension, or discomfort into healing images. Make use of all your senses since they're extremely powerful.

Begin by attending to the area of your body where the worst pain is located. Ask yourself the following questions:

- If I were to draw a picture of my pain, associating it with some object or condition, what would that picture be? Tight-knotted nautical ropes, perhaps, or a murky, stagnant pool?

- Is there a sound connected with the problem or pain? A grinding, perhaps, or gurgling?

- Is there a texture associated with it? A sore throat, for instance, might feel like sandpaper; an upset stomach might feel slimy.

- Is there a temperature associated with it? A headache might feel hot; a broken limb might feel cold.

- Is there a smell or taste associated with it?

- Is there a movement associated with it? Churning, stabbing, pounding?

Now, "flip" these images. The essential consideration is what the problem or pain will look, feel, smell, sound, and taste like when it is alleviated or cured. For each image you formed in answering the previous questions, you'll now substitute its opposite. For example, those knotted ropes are slowly untied and loosely laid on the deck; the stagnant pool is drained and filled with clear, sweet water; the dark cloud of pain in your head is penetrated with sunlight; the pounding sound is replaced by the sound of a waterfall.

As you relax, substitute a positive, healing image for each negative, painful one. Use words, if necessary, to reinforce this. Post a sign or note near you to remind yourself to flip often into a new set of images. Don't be discouraged if you can't conjure all the images suggested. Use the ones that are strongest for you, and be patient with yourself in anticipating results.

From *The Fine Art of Recuperation, A Guide to Surviving and Thriving After Illness, Accident or Surgery* by Regina Sara Ryan. © 1991. Jeremy P. Tarcher Publishing/Putnam Publishing Group, Los Angeles, CA $9.95 (presently out of print). For a complete catalog of Jeremy Tarcher titles, including several related to self-help and the healing process, call (213) 935-9980.

108
DEALING WITH SURGERY

It may surprise you to learn that just about everyone has the same fears about surgery. After all, operations scar. The mere thought of anesthesia raises fears of being helpless and surrendering to blades or instruments that invade the body. No doubt you're afraid you might never awaken; and even if you do, you're uncertain to what: vomiting and dizziness, which may follow anesthesia, extensive changes in your appearance or feeling of your body, sexual impotence, or indifference to sex. These many questions, most of them unanswerable, can make the days preceding surgery a period of suspicion and dejection, all heightened by a generalized terror of death.

Here then are some suggestions to help reduce your fears:

- Insist your doctor thoroughly explains the surgical procedure and everything that follows.

- Consider seeking a second opinion.

- Be frank in discussing your fears with the surgeon.

- Don't be disappointed if your surgeon's not warm and outgoing.

- Ask to meet the anesthesiologist.

- Treat the nurse who performs the preoperative workup as a valuable information resource.

- Express any fears or concerns you may have immediately after surgery to the nurses in the recovery room.

- Remember that panic in the first few days after surgery is a normal reaction, as is anger, depression, and, in some patients, hallucinations.

Surgery exacts a price, in pain as well as in fear; but the price is none too high when the surgeon cuts you free from your affliction.

From *You Can Make It Back: Coping With Serious Illness* by Paul M. Levitt and Elissa S. Guralnick. © 1985. Facts on File Publications, New York, NY $16.95. Currently out of print but still available at many libraries. (212) 683-2244.

109

AIR LIFT FOR FEAR

If you're feeling especially frightened or confused, here's a relaxation exercise that might help "lift" your fears away:

Bring your awareness into the present by listening to the sounds around you, both inside and outside the room. Let them come and go.

Bring your attention to the top of your head and imagine a wave of relaxation beginning to flow through that area of your body, melting away all tension. Allow the wave to flow downward through each part of your body, jaw, neck, shoulders, etc. Use your attention to systematically go through your body, from head to foot, until every part is relaxed. If you want, try to breathe relaxation in through the top of your head and breathe tension out through the bottoms of your feet.

When you have been through your whole body, take a couple of deep breaths. As you breathe out, allow yourself to feel more and more deeply relaxed.

You can either rest in this state for a while or go on to the next steps.

Imagine yourself in a beautiful, natural place; it may be a place you know or a completely imaginary place. Absorb the peace and beauty of this place. Note the details of everything around you. What is the ground like beneath your feet? What does the air feel like against your skin in this place, etc.

Imagine there are some balloons nearby, and one by one you tie each of your problems and fears to a balloon and watch it float away.

As you watch the last balloon float off, feel the sun's golden warmth on your head and shoulders. Allow its golden radiance to warm and soothe your whole body, particularly the painful or diseased areas.

Gradually bring yourself back. Become aware of your body and the room you are in, and in your own time, open your eyes.

From *Coping with Cancer; Making Sense of It All* by Rachael Clyne. © 1989. Thorsons Publishing Group/HarperCollins Publishing, Wellingborough, England and New York, NY. (212) 207-7000.

110

TAKE THIS JOURNEY INTO DEEP RELAXATION

Take a very deep breath and quiet your mind. I want you to imagine being on the sandy beach of a peaceful tropical island. Visualize the scenes I am describing to the very best of your ability, mentally creating every detail of these pictures in your mind. Make them real; perceive the sounds and smells that accompany your impressions, and sense the feeling this environment generates within you.

It's almost sunrise...the sky is just dark enough for you to see the last few stars...The palm trees that line this tropical beach are silhouetted against the sky. Experience the fresh salt sea air ...you are totally at peace here. All your mental and physical desires are satisfied and you experience this environment in total peace.

So watch the stars...the palm trees...totally experience this peaceful environment. And as you do, feel your physical body relaxing...beginning with both of your feet at the same time. Feel your feet relaxing . . . and the relaxing power moves up into your lower legs, relaxing all your muscles as it goes. And up into your upper legs . . . permeating every cell and every atom.

The sky is becoming lighter and lighter. All is silent but the calls of the sea gulls and the lapping waves. The stars are slowly fading away. As you observe this beautiful environment, you feel the relaxing power in the fingers of your hand. Relaxing your hands. Feel your hands relaxing and feel the relaxing power move into your forearms. And up to your upper arms. Just completely relaxing your fingers, hands, forearms, and upper arms.

You now become more aware of the sea gulls announcing the new day...as the darkness slowly fades away and the sky becomes lighter...bluer...bluer. The horizon now begins to glow red. And then yellow golden. The first rays of the sun touch the tops of the palm trees. And now as the sun slowly rises, watch the light illuminating the palms as it moves down the trunk of the tree. And within, you feel a warmth in your spine, as the relaxing power flows through your spine, and into your back muscles, relaxing your back. It moves up into your neck and shoulder muscles, which now become loose and limp. Loose and limp. Just completely relaxed.

Now the sun falls across your body, bathing you in a golden light. You shiver in response as you absorb the essence and energy. Feel the sun on your skin and perceive it filling your body to overflowing with energy. The relaxing power now moves up the back of your neck and into your scalp, relaxing your scalp. It drains down into your facial muscles, relaxing your facial muscles. Your jaw is relaxed. Allow a little space between your teeth. Your throat is relaxed. Your entire body is now relaxed all over in every way. Now notice how the sun reflects on the surface of the water: sparkling, sparkling yellow and gold. Flickering reflections of the sun that is now rising into the yellow golden sky sparkle on the water.

Enjoy this environment. You can swim or walk along the beach. Or simply lie back in the warm sand. And as you do, you'll begin to hear a sound that will relax you even more...even more...even more.

You're now relaxed and at ease, in total control. At this relaxed level, your subconscious mind is open and receptive to positive suggestions:

You are relaxed and at ease, relaxed and at ease, relaxed and at ease. You detach from worldly pressures and retreat to a calm inner space. Every day in every way, you become more peaceful and harmonious. You accept other people as they are, without expectations. You handle your responsibilities with harmonious ease. Negativity flows through you without affecting you. You peacefully accept the things you cannot change and change the things you can. You are at peace with yourself, the world, and everyone in it.

From Stress Control: RX17 Digital-Holophonic™ Audio Cassette by Dick Sutphen. Valley of the Sun, Malibu, CA (800) 225-4717.

JOURNEYING THROUGH THE WORLD OF HEALTH CARE

Nature, time, and patience are the three great physicians.

—Henry George Bohn

If you mean to keep as well as possible, the less you think about your health, the better.

—Oliver Wendell Holmes, Sr.

The best medicine I know for rheumatism is to thank the Lord that it ain't gout.

—Josh Billings

DOCTORING YOUR HEALTH

"O.K. Who else needs an operation before
I put this stuff away?"

111

THE SEE-THROUGH HOSPITAL

If you become a hospital patient, it helps to know how hospitals are organized. A typical metropolitan "teaching" hospital can serve as a model.

First and foremost are the *physicians*, starting with the *medical board of directors* at the top, followed by *committee chairmen* and then *department chiefs*—though you will rarely, if ever, meet any of these people.

Medical and legal responsibility for your treatment lies with your *attending physician*, who is usually a board-certified specialist. In the case of an oncologist, for instance, he or she has a 3-year residency in internal medicine plus 2 to 4 years of specialized training (or a "fellowship") in the causes and treatment of cancer.

In a large teaching hospital, many people report to your attending specialist. Most immediately are the *fellows in training,* ranking downward from fourth, third, second or first year in seniority. Below these are *medical* or *surgical residents* and any *medical students,* ranked according to experience. While some of these physicians and students make limited decisions about your treatment, the ultimate authority and responsibility lies with the attending physician. You need to know this when you want something done, particularly something out of the ordinary.

So much for who gives the orders; next are those who carry them out. Most noticeably, this means the nurses—especially the *chief nurse* of your unit or ward and the *staff nurses*. Their goodwill most immediately affects your experience as a patient. The one who administers the moment-by-moment operation of your ward or unit is the *head* or *"charge" nurse.* You can expect your head nurse to be a fully dedicated professional—a good administrator who will also do everything possible to alleviate your pain or stress. The head nurse is a role model for the younger staff nurses who care for you on a day-to-day basis, working very hard in your behalf.

Nurses get some reward from observing your progress. But also remember how good it feels to be appreciated: A simple "please" and "thank you" goes a long way.

The same applies to dealings with all hospital staff: *x-ray technicians, ward clerks, housekeeping personnel, aides, "transporters,"* etc. You can be pretty sure that hospital workers enjoy helping people or they wouldn't be there. But because doctors are the most visible and get most of the credit, all the others so essential to your welfare can easily be overlooked. That's why it's particularly important to be liberal in thanking them. You will also be treated better in return.

From *The Diagnosis is Cancer* by Edward J. Larschan. © 1979. Bull Publishing, Menlo Park, CA $9.95. (800) 676-2855.

112
TESTING 1-2-3

The best (and most comforting) guide to medical tests is *The People's Book of Medical Tests,* by David S. Sobel, M.D. and Tom Ferguson, M.D. © 1985. Summit Books, New York, NY $12.95. (212) 698-7000. It's highly recommend if you anticipate having any tests before, during, or after your hospitalization or recuperation.

113
PATIENT ASSERTIVENESS

Sometimes people who are recuperating may need to be more assertive and ask for what they need. If you feel your doctor is spending too little time with you, see that you receive a longer appointment on your next visit. But come prepared with the specific items you wish to discuss. Being straightforward about your questions and concerns makes it easier for the doctor to give the appropriate responses. The following questions will provide a starting point:

- What's wrong with me?
- What treatment do you recommend?
- What are the objectives of treatment?
- How will the treatment affect my condition?
- What are the risks and side effects of the recommended treatment?
- How much will treatment cost?
- Are there alternative treatments?

If you feel your doctor does not answer any of these questions completely, ask more questions. To the greatest degree possible, you need to know what to expect in the months and years ahead. So, be persistent.

From *I Can Cope* by Judith L. Johnson, R.N., Ph.D. and Linda Klein. © 1994. CHRONIMED Publishing, Minneapolis, MN $9.95. (800) 444-5951.

114

ACTIVE VS. PASSIVE

People who are actively involved in their medical care do better than those who are passive. To find out if you and your doctor are communicating effectively, answer these five simple questions:

1) Does your doctor seem impatient or hurried when you start discussing your questions?

2) Do you abbreviate or rush your questions so you won't keep the doctor waiting when he or she has so many other people to see?

3) Are your questions met with vague, long-winded, or evasive answers?

4) Are you unable to explain to friends and family what your doctor told you?

5) Are you relieved to be able to turn to nurses, nurses' aides, or orderlies to explain things to you?

If the answer is "yes" to any of the above, try these phrases to enhance communication and understanding with your doctor:

- "Why no, doctor, I don't understand that part very well. Can you please explain that last part again?"

- "Well, what are you really telling me I can expect next?"

- "I'd appreciate it if you could list my options for me."

- "Excuse me, doctor, but I think it would help me to have my (husband/wife/friend) here for this discussion, so I'd like to wait until they're here."

From *What Your Doctor Didn't Learn in Medical School...And What You Can Do About It* by Stuart M. Berger, M.D. ©1988. William Morrow & Company, New York, NY $18.95. (212) 261-6500.

115
DOCTORTALK 101

Your doctor is a channel through which you get access to medicine, surgery, and other treatments that affect your health. To get what you need, it's good to learn how to interact with your doctor effectively...

- Before your appointment, make a list of things you want the doctor to know and any questions you need answered. Don't leave the meeting until those subjects have been covered to your satisfaction—even if you have to repeat your questions several times.

- Remember that a meeting with your doctor is not a social conversation. Don't worry about being entertaining or bouncing the conversational ball back and forth.

- Keep each question or statement to less than 20 seconds. Research shows the longest period of time doctors allow patients to talk before interrupting them is 18 seconds.

- Don't try to talk like a doctor. If you've been feeling short of breath, say so—don't say you have dyspena. Using medical jargon may be taken as a challenge; the doctor may try to top you by using even more technical language, and you won't get your questions answered.

From an interview with linguist Suzette Haden Elgin, Ph.D., author of *Staying Well with the Gentle Art of Verbal Self Defense.* © 1990. Prentice Hall Business and Professional Publishing, Englewood Cliffs, NJ $12.95. (201) 592-2000. Reprinted with permission from *Bottom Line Personal,* 330 W. 42nd St., New York, NY 10036. 24 issues per year/$49 per year or $4 per issue. (800) 274-5611.

116
DEMANDING YOUR RIGHTS

According to the American Hospital Association's official Patient's Bill of Rights, a patient has the right to:

- Considerate and respectful care.

- Receive from a physician the information necessary to give informed consent before any procedure or treatment is started, and to know the name of the person responsible for the procedure or treatment.

- Refuse treatment to the extent you are permitted by law, and to be informed of all the possible medical consequences of the refusal.

- Privacy concerning your medical care, including your medical records and communications. People who are not directly involved in your care must have permission to be present during any procedure or treatment.

- Make reasonable requests for services and to receive a complete explanation if you're being transferred to another facility.

- Know what financial arrangement the hospital has with other health care facilities to which they may refer you for care and whether your doctor has a financial stake in the laboratories or testing centers he or she uses.

- Be informed if the hospital plans to engage in or perform human experiments that pertain to your care and to refuse to be involved in any experiments.

- Expect continuity of care and information about follow-up after leaving the hospital.

- Examine and receive explanations of hospital bills, regardless of the source of payment.

- Know any hospital rules and regulations that apply to the patient's conduct.

From "Your Guide to Getting Good Hospital Care" by Tim Friend. © *USA Today*, June 19, 1991. Reprinted with permission. $107 per year for 5 issues per week. (800) 872-0001.

117
STUDY YOUR INSURANCE PLAN

Even before you begin to be treated, you should study your policy and meet with your company's benefits officer, or call the agent who sold you the plan, to determine what costs will be covered. You should know, for example, if your policy will pay for:

- unlimited hospitalization
- a private room (or the cost difference between a private and semi-private room)
- a private nurse
- doctor's fees
- therapy or psychiatric counseling
- rehabilitation
- equipment—such as a dialysis unit—for use in the home
- cosmetic surgery for reconstruction or to change a limb or face altered by surgery or disease
- prosthetic limbs or body parts
- dental care
- prescription drugs

The more familiar you are with your policy's provisions, the more information you can give your doctor that may affect your "bottom line." You may find your doctor can adjust your treatment plan to take maximum advantage of your coverage.

From *You Can Make It Back: Coping With Serious Illness* by Paul M. Levitt and Elissa S. Guralnick. © 1985. Facts on File Publications, New York, NY $16.95. Currently out of print but still available at many libraries. (212) 683-2244.

118
THE MISSING LINK

Many hospitals have an ombudsman or guest relations program that provides a specially trained representative who can run interference for you, respond to any special needs, or answer any questions. If the hospital does not offer this service, try the Social Work Department if you have a problem that cannot be straightened out.

119
TO TREAT OR NOT TO TREAT

When a treatment is routine or minor, the decision to accept it isn't difficult. But when you're certain a treatment will cause sacrifice or pain, offers no guarantee of a cure, causes disfigurement, or subjects you to the risk of lethal side effects, the decision requires you to rearrange your mind and seek the approval of your friends. As you grapple with your choices, you might want to take the following steps:

Compare the probable consequences of accepting treatment with those of refusing it. In particular, after you've consulted with your doctor, answer these 10 questions:

1. What physical limitations are you likely to face if you are treated and if you are not?

2. Will these limitations be permanent or temporary?

3. What rehabilitation services will be available to you, if you're treated and if you're not?

4. How much improvement is rehabilitation likely to achieve?

5. What changes will occur in your self-esteem, if you're treated and if you're not?

6. What sexual adjustments will have to be made, if you're treated and if you're not?

7. What pleasures and habits will have to be sacrificed, if you're treated and if you're not?

8. How will your life or job have to change, if you're treated and if you're not?

9. Whose regard are you likely to lose or maintain, if you're treated and if you're not?

10. Are you facing a serious threat to your life, if you're treated and if you're not?

Unless you can answer every question—from facts and not preconceived opinions—you aren't prepared to decide if you want to be treated. In gathering the facts about treatment, it may also help to talk with other patients who have undergone the treatment you are facing, as well as friends, family, clergy, or counseling professionals, such as social workers or psychologists.

From *You Can Make It Back: Coping With Serious Illness* by Paul M. Levitt and Elissa S. Guralnick. © 1985. Facts on File Publications, New York, NY $16.95. Currently out of print but still available in many libraries. (212) 683-2244.

120

HOW TO TREAT YOUR TREATMENT PLAN

Keep in mind that cooperation with your treatment does not mean blind obedience. If you disagree with your treatment plan, tell your doctor. If your doctor suggests a plan that is impractical for you, discuss it. Come to some understanding with each other. Usually, many more options are available than are immediately apparent. Explore alternatives. Accepting treatment recommendations passively and then resisting them actively is a waste of your precious time and effort.

From *The Fine Art of Recuperation, A Guide to Surviving and Thriving After Illness, Accident or Surgery* by Regina Sara Ryan. © 1991. Jeremy P. Tarcher Publishing/Putnam Publishing Group, Los Angeles, CA $9.95 (presently out of print). For a complete catalog of Jeremy Tarcher titles, including several related to self-help and the healing process, call (213) 935-9980.

121

MAKING THE ROUNDS

In any kind of hospital, large or small, the disclosure of personal information is necessary, if regretful. So is the uncovering of your body and your submission to hands that search and probe. Still, even if you have to concede these violations of privacy, you can certainly demand that hospital rounds and medical records, in particular, be designed so you do not feel humiliated. You should take to task, politely but firmly, the doctor who:

- treats you like an object

- ridicules your questions

- speaks in jargon-ridden phrases

- whispers to his or her colleagues frightening comments you overhear

You should also object when bedcharts containing confidential comments are hung beside your bed for everyone to see. Rounds should be an exercise not only in skillful diagnosis, but also in a kindly bedside manner. And bedcharts that disclose how you're coping, or how likely you are to be cured, should always be written with tact and treated as confidential.

From *You Can Make It Back: Coping With Serious Illness* by Paul M. Levitt and Elissa S. Guralnick. © 1985. Facts on File Publications, New York, NY $16.95. Currently out of print but still available in many libraries. (212) 683-2244.

122
DEAR DIARY

Sometimes it's helpful to keep a diary for the next time you see your doctor. In the diary, be sure to include any activity that increases or decreases your pain. Also, include how frequently you take your pain medication and the amount taken. In addition, note if you use the medication before the pain starts or only once you're already in pain. Finally, be sure to assign a number from 1 (no pain) to 10 (the worst pain you can imagine) that best describes your pain.

From *I Can Cope* by Judith L. Johnson, R.N., Ph.D. and Linda Klein. © 1994. CHRONIMED Publishing, Minneapolis, MN $9.95 (800) 444-5951.

123
NURSES: A FIRST-CLASS RESOURCE

It may not be apparent to you at first, but nurses are not just caregivers. They are prepared—assuming you ask them during times they're free—to do all of the following:

Explain the nature of your illness. Nurses know the organs of the body, their functions, and afflictions, just as doctors do; and because they're trained to act as patient-advocates, they're often better able than a doctor to describe your illness in language you can understand.

Review the details of your treatment. Nurses can explain to you not only the nature of your treatment, but also how the treatment will proceed: how, for example, you'll be prepared for surgery; who will transport you to the operating room; and when you'll be returned to your hospital bed. The forewarning may disarm your anxiety.

Evaluate the side effects of treatment. If a test, procedure, or drug causes discomfort, don't wait until you see your doctor to complain. You should advise a nurse immediately. She or he will know the significance of the side effects you're suffering, and also how to give some relief, if an antidote exists.

Discuss your condition with your doctor. Because nurses can observe you through all of an 8-hour shift, as a doctor cannot, they're uniquely suited to describe how your symptoms rise and abate, how you respond to medication, and how often and severely you feel pain.

Give comfort to you and your family. Though it's true that nurses often engage in technical tasks, they're nonetheless as competent at caring as at curing, and can quiet fears or fill a lonely void.

Teach you how to care for your condition. Before you're released from the hospital, your nurses can help you learn any tasks you'll have to perform for yourself; for example, dressing a wound; irrigating a colostomy; administering eyedrops or using a salve; checking your pulse; or slipping into clothing when a part of your body is sore or immobile.

124

MEDICATION SMARTS

It's important to take all pain medication properly. Be sure to follow exactly your doctor's directions, including taking each dose as scheduled and finishing the entire prescription. Skipping even one dose "on a good day" can considerably increase your pain later.

From *Coping With Pain—The Battle Half Won* by the Arthritis Foundation, P.O. Box 19000, Atlanta, GA 30326 Free. (404) 872-7100.

125

WHY BEING LABELED UNCOOPERATIVE MAY BE GOOD FOR YOUR HEALTH

"Uncooperative patients" get better faster. To a doctor, uncooperative means asking many questions, being persistent, researching one's illness, and examining one's medical records. Yet patients who are more knowledgeable about their condition and participate in the decision-making process receive more satisfactory care from their physicians.

Katherine Lindner, M.L.S., R.N., Englewood, NJ, writing in the *Journal of the American Medical Association,* 515 N. State St., Chicago, IL 60510. 48 issues. $95/yr. (312) 464-5000. Reprinted with permission from *Bottom Line Personal,* 330 W. 42nd St., New York, NY 10036. 24 issues per year/$49 per year or $4 per issue. (800) 274-5611.

126
WHEN YOU'RE SICK ALL OVER AGAIN

W hen an early treatment fails to cure, it doesn't matter why. Whether the treatment was too gentle, the illness too insidious, or the chance of cure too small, the persistence or recurrence of your illness breaks your spirit. Recurrence, in particular, can overwhelm you. You feel that you've been twice betrayed: your body's fallen ill, and then pretended to be cured, only to succumb again to illness. No wonder you're angrier than ever, and longing to surrender. If you're:

- guilty with fear that you're unworthy of health

- sleepless

- depressed

- anxious or restless

- quick to lose your temper and

- uninterested in eating,

then your condition is perfectly normal—and perfectly counterproductive.

As dreadful as the task may be, you have to find the strength to reach a sensible decision about how you will proceed. You must accept another treatment or reject it; and unless you want your family to decide the matter for you, these are a few questions you must answer:

- How much can the new treatment accomplish?

- Does the treatment involve any appreciable risks?

- How have other patients responded to the treatment?

- Has your emotional response to earlier treatment revealed any hidden strengths or weaknesses?

- What advice are you receiving from the people whom you turn to for support?

In illness, as in every other feature of your life, it's useful to have had some experience. Though no one would choose to be sick in the first place, nor choose to fall sick again and again, the second and subsequent battles with illness, though hard because you're weary, may go well because you're seasoned. If you look to your experience, instead of your fatigue, you'll find the means to do what you must do.

From *You Can Make It Back: Coping With Serious Illness* by Paul M. Levitt and Elissa S. Guralnick. © 1985. Facts on File Publications, New York, NY $16.95. Currently out of print but still available in many libraries. (212) 683-2244.

GREAT MEDICAL MOMENTS

"Gesundheit."

155

127

EASING POST-SURGERY URINATION

One of the most common post-surgical side effects of general anesthesia is difficulty or inability urinating. To "inspire" your body back to normal, hold your hand under warm running water while sitting on the toilet. If you can only use a bedpan, put one hand in a basin of warm water on a bedside table and move your hand around slowly.

128

THE AUDIO RECOVERY ROOM

If you anticipate having surgery, take a small tape player with headphones and a tape to the hospital so you can listen to reassuring messages and positive affirming comments about your recovery *during surgery.* It can greatly increase your ability to recover promptly and will lessen pain or bleeding. (Just remember to tell your surgeon and your anesthesiologist that you'd like to use a tape player.)

From an interview with clinical psychologist, John Hudesman, Ph.D. Reprinted with permission from *Bottom Line Personal,* 330 W. 42nd St., New York, NY 10036. 24 issues per year/$49 per year or $4 per issue. (800) 274-5611.

129
BREAKING THE MONOTONY OF LYING STILL

Some hospital procedures require lying still in uncomfortable positions for a long time. Try these suggestions for relieving the boredom and stress:

- focus on points in the room to provide a diversion

- daydream about wonderful travel experiences, loving memories, or pleasant thoughts

- wiggle your toes or any part of your body you can in a rotating manner

From *Successful Living with Chronic Illness* by Kathleen Lewis. ©1989. Avery Publishing Group, Garden City Park, NY $10. To order: (404) 491-6850.

130
PRESSURE POINT

Assuming it doesn't create additional stress for you to monitor your blood pressure, you might want to consider a watch that also records blood pressure. The Casio BP-100 watch can give you an approximate blood pressure reading anytime and anywhere. Simply place two fingers over the watch's sensor, hold for 30 seconds, and receive an estimation of your diastolic and systolic blood pressure shown on its LCD screen. It takes up to 30 separate readings along with the date and time, and stores them in the watch's memory so you can keep close track of your blood pressure history over days or weeks. A bar graph that visually displays the ups and downs of your last 21 readings can also be recalled on the readout. Other regular watch functions include time, date, alarm, stopwatch, and display backlight. $139.95 from Hammacher Schlemmer, (800) 543-3366. Or write the Hammacher Schlemmer Operations Center, 2515 E. 43rd St., P.O. Box 182256, Chattanooga, TN 37422.

131
HELP FOR COLD HANDS/COLD FEET

An extra pair of socks can help cover cold hands or cold feet in possibly cool hospital temperatures. Take several pair along with you or ask a friend or relative to retrieve them if you forget. The nurse may also be able to provide you with a pair.

From *Successful Living With Chronic Illness* by Kathleen Lewis. © 1989. Avery Publishing Group, Garden City Park, NY $10. To order: (404) 491-6850.

132
OSTOMY ABCS

If you have to deal with a colostomy, ileostomy, or urostomy, there's an excellent book that can help. *Coping With an Ostomy* by psychologist Robert Phillips, M.D., offers meaningful advice and information. The book is available from many public libraries or from Avery Publishing Group for $8.95. (800) 548-5757.

133

THE PHARMACY OF LAUGHTER

The brain acts as its own pharmacy, producing more than 50 psychoactive drugs that affect memory, intelligence, sedation, and aggression.

Endorphin, for example, is the brain's version of the painkiller morphine, but it is three times more powerful. These natural painkillers are frequently released during physical exercise, such as long-distance running and laughter. (This may be why laughing makes us feel so good. And why you should do it as often as possible.)

From *The Compass in Your Nose* by Marc McCutcheon. © 1989. Jeremy P. Tarcher Publishing/Putnam Publishing Group, Los Angeles, CA $8.95. (213) 935-9980.

134

HAVE A GOOD YAWN

Today doctors believe the feeling of rejuvenation we get after a good yawn comes not from increased oxygen but from the expulsion of excess carbon dioxide in the blood. A hearty yawn improves circulation by stretching and contracting the muscles of the neck and chest. People who are severely ill tend to refrain from yawning until their condition improves. Physicians often recognize a yawn as one of the first signs of recovery.

From *The Compass in Your Nose* by Marc McCutcheon. © 1989. Jeremy P. Tarcher Publishing/Putnam Publishing Group, Los Angeles, CA $8.95. (213) 935-9980.

135

OH COMFORT OF COMFORTERS

Whenever I've had to face surgery or a hospital stay, I make sure I bring either my fuzzy fake chinchilla blanket from home or a quilt that I particularly like. A good resource for down comforters and sheets of every size and shape is The Company Store catalog (800) 323-8000. For dazzling colorful sheets and comforters, try the Domestications catalog (800) 782-7722. And for fake animal fur throws like my chinchilla, try A Touch of Class catalog (812) 683-3707.

136
PRIVACY PLEASE!

W hen hospitals violate your privacy, don't hesitate to ask why. You should also insist on preserving what privacy you can. If you suffer in silence and speak only to please others, no one will hear your complaint. But if you speak what you feel, you may find that you get what you want.

From *You Can Make It Back: Coping With Serious Illness* by Paul M. Levitt and Elissa S. Guralnick. © 1985. Facts on File Publications, New York, NY $16.95. Currently out of print but still available in many libraries. (212) 683-2244.

137

EIGHT MOVIES NEVER TO WATCH UNTIL YOU FEEL A LOT BETTER

1. **Bad Medicine**. The adventures of students attending a "Mickey Mouse" med school in Central America. When they find the health conditions in a nearby village unacceptable, they start a medical clinic, stealing the needed drugs from the school's pharmacy.

2. **Britannia Hospital**. A wildly inadequate hospital serves as a metaphor for an ailing society in this (hopefully) improbably black comedy.

3. **Critical Condition**. While under observation in a psychiatric ward of a major hospital, Richard Pryor finds himself in charge of the institution.

4. **Dead Ringers**. Jeremy Irons plays twin gynecologists who are addicted to drugs, sex, and increasingly disturbing ideas about their patients.

5. **The Hospital**. George C. Scott is an embittered doctor battling the outrageous goings-on at the institution of the title.

6. **Men in Black.** The Three Stooges in an Academy Award-winning short film parody of those glamorous "men in white."

7. **The Terrible Two-Headed Transplant.** Ray Milland, a loathsome bigot, finds his head transplanted onto Rosie Grier, who objects strenuously.

8. **Vital Signs.** A father and son surgical team fight their double addictions to drugs and alcohol. Stars Ed Asner and Gary Cole.

From *The Video Movie Guide* by Mick Martin, Marsha Porter, and Ed Remitz. ©1993. Ballantine Books, New York, NY $6.95. (800) 733-3000.

EDIBLE STRATEGIES

"You need more exercise.
Go and get me a cheeseburger with onions."

138
SWEET RX

Chocolate contains phenylethylamine, the same chemical the brain produces when people fall in love. The chemical causes a happy, slightly dreamy feeling by stepping up the heart rate and the body's energy level.

So, assuming you don't have a problem such as high cholesterol or diabetes, and assuming you're not on a low-fat or caffeine-free diet, you may want to ask your doctor if it's OK for you to indulge in this natural mood elevator.

From *The Compass In Your Nose* by Marc McCutcheon. © 1989. Jeremy P. Tarcher Publishing/Putnam Publishing Group, Los Angeles, CA $8.95. (213) 935-9980.

139

GIVING NUTRITION A BOOST

Despite their best efforts, some people are still unable to get enough protein and calories into their daily diet. Because adequate nutrition is essential during recuperation or treatments, most doctors and nurses recommend a commercial nutritional supplement such as Ensure® to those people. Many different brands of supplements are available, either at a pharmacy or grocery store. Those interested should ask their doctor or nurse to make a recommendation.

From *I Can Cope* by Judith L. Johnson, R.N., Ph.D. and Linda Klein. © 1994. CHRONIMED Publishing, Minneapolis, MN $9.95. (800) 444-5951.

140

SET THE MOOD FOR FOOD

Even when you start feeling better after an accident or injury, food may still not sound appealing. Many people have found the following techniques make eating easier and more enjoyable:

- Create the right atmosphere. If you're standing alone at the kitchen counter, it's easy to decide against eating, even though you know you should. Making meals a social affair stimulates the appetite. Set the table with placemats and flowers. Play pleasant dinner music, and perhaps invite family and friends to join you. You'll be more relaxed and may discover you are more hungry than you thought.

- With your doctor's approval, have a glass of wine or beer before a meal. It's relaxing and can also be an appetite stimulant. Good odors may help, too. The smell of a fresh loaf of bread or cake baking can make you hungry for those foods.

- Take advantage of the "up" times. Eat well when you're feeling good. This is also a good time to prepare meals that can be frozen and easily reheated on your more difficult days.

- When you're feeling good, eat whenever you're hungry, even if it isn't mealtime. Many of the nutrients you consume at these times will be stored for later use.

- Make use of timesavers. Some people don't have a problem with eating while recuperating at home, but they often feel too tired to cook. If this is the case, consider the following suggestions:

  Let someone else do the cooking.

  Prepare a list of people who can shop, cook, set the table, and clean up for you, and then call on these people to help you.

On high-energy days, cook large batches of food that can be frozen and used later. Add instructions so others can help you.

Prepare and post a weekly menu, including items that can be easily put together. Simple casseroles, hot dogs, hamburgers, frozen pizza, or TV dinners are all good and easy.

Accept gifts of food and offers of help from family and friends. If you can't use the food right away, freeze it.

Use paper plates, paper napkins, and disposable silverware as often as possible to save on dishwashing. Use disposable pans for cooking (foil containers from frozen dinners work well).

- Keep snacks on hand. Good ideas for easy snacks are ice cream, peanut butter and crackers, pudding, peanuts, dried fruits, and canned milk shakes.

- Eat small, frequent meals. Instead of planning on three meals a day, eat just a little bit at a time, but more often. If weight loss has been a problem, be sure to ask yourself every 2 hours or so if you've eaten something lately. By eating nutritious snacks every few hours throughout the day, you can probably meet your needs without too much effort.

- Treat yourself frequently to your favorite foods. Plan your weekly menus around foods that have always been your favorite.

- At mealtime, eat solid foods before liquids. Liquids may fill you up before you have met your nutritional needs. Save the liquids for after the meal.

From *I Can Cope* by Judith L. Johnson, R.N., Ph.D. and Linda Klein. © 1994. CHRONIMED Publishing, Minneapolis, MN $9.95. (800) 444-5951.

141
SIDELINING SIDE EFFECTS

In addition to loss of appetite, people recuperating from an illness or injury, or undergoing chemotherapy, may experience other side effects that interfere with the enjoyment of eating. Here are some possible solutions to the side effects mentioned most often.

To Relieve Feelings of Fullness
- Eat small, more frequent meals.
- Chew foods slowly.
- Limit greasy foods, butter, and sauces.
- Drink nutritional liquids.
- Limit liquid intake with meals.

To Relieve Nausea and Vomiting
- Serve food at room temperature.
- Take an anti-nausea medicine 30 minutes to an hour before eating.
- Eat small portions of low-fat foods, such as applesauce or Jell-O.
- Avoid nauseating food smells—cold tuna salad is a good source of protein and has little odor.
- Eat salty foods and avoid sweet foods.
- Eat dry foods (toast or crackers) in the morning.
- Drink clear, cool beverages (pop, juice, Kool-Aid).
- Rest after eating, but do not lie down flat for at least 2 hours.
- Avoid greasy fried foods, both because of the smells and because they are difficult to digest.

To Relieve Mouth and Throat Problems

- Avoid highly-acidic and spicy foods, such as oranges or pizza.

- Try a softer diet. Many favorite foods can be put in a blender while they're still warm and come out tasting very good.

- Eat food lukewarm rather than hot or cold.

- Avoid alcohol and tobacco.

- Use a straw to make drinking easier.

- Soak foods in your beverage before eating. For example, soaking bread in milk makes it easier to chew and swallow.

- Avoid citrus fruit juices (grapefruit, pineapple, and orange).

- Assuming your doctor says it's OK, try the following foods, which are usually well-tolerated: custards, Popsicles, puddings, milk shakes, ice cream, eggnog, gelatins.

- Use butter, gravies, or sauces on food whenever possible.

- Suck on sugarless candy or ice chips.

To Relieve a Bitter or Metallic Taste

- If meat doesn't taste right, substitute chicken, turkey, eggs (if you're not on a low cholesterol diet) or dairy products.

- Eat foods that leave their own tastes in your mouth, such as fresh fruits or hard candies.

- Drink more liquids.

- Eat foods cool or at room temperature. They'll taste better.

- To add flavor to meats, marinate them in sweet fruit juices, sweet wines, or Italian dressing.

- If you're not having problems with a sour mouth or throat, try strongly flavored foods, such as pizza, tacos, or barbecued chicken.

To Relieve Diarrhea

- Avoid foods with high fiber, such as fresh fruits and vegetables or whole-grain cereals and breads.

- Consume fluids between meals, not during meals.

- Eat small, frequent meals.

- Serve foods warm or at room temperature.

- Avoid gas-forming foods such as beer, beans, cabbage, broccoli, cauliflower, gum, coffee, and too many sweets.

- Try the following foods, they may help: applesauce, cheese, cottage cheese, gelatin, toast, tea.

To Relieve Constipation

- Include a variety of fiber-rich foods in your diet: fruit, vegetables, whole grains, nuts, and popcorn.

- Add 1 or 2 tablespoons of bran to foods.

- Include prunes and prune juice in your daily diet. They may act as a mild laxative.

- Drink plenty of fluids. Hot liquids will stimulate bowel activity.

- Ask your doctor to prescribe a laxative or stool softener.

From *I Can Cope* by Judith L. Johnson, R.N., Ph.D. and Linda Klein. © 1994.
CHRONIMED Publishing, Minneapolis, MN $9.95. (800) 444-5951.

142
HELP FOR "DRY MOUTH"

If NPO (nothing by mouth) has been written on your chart because of surgery, a procedure, or a health problem, and you have dry mouth as a result, here are some helpful suggestions to follow once you get your doctor's or nurse's okay:

- Rinse your mouth with mouthwash or brush your teeth, being careful not to swallow.

- Suck a slightly damp clean washcloth, letting dry mucous membranes absorb the moisture.

- Keep lips moistened with lip balm.

- Drink plenty of fluids right up to the time for the "NPO" to begin.

- Ask for a vaporizer.

From *Successful Living with Chronic Illness* by Kathleen Lewis. © 1989. Avery Publishing Group, Garden City Park, NY $10. To order: (404) 491-6850.

ENTERTAINING YOURSELF WITH DIVERSIONS AND DISTRACTIONS

I enjoy convalescence. It is the part that makes the illness worthwhile.

—George Bernard Shaw

The art of medicine consists of amusing the patient while nature cures the disease.

—Voltaire

There are people who strictly deprive themselves of each and every eatable, drinkable, and smokable which has in any way acquired a shady reputation. They pay this price for health, and health is all they get for it.

—Mark Twain

THE BEST BEST BOREDOM BUSTERS
OF ALL TIME

9-4

"I think we can unhook the VCR."

143
VIDEO VISITS

Why wait until you have enough money to take the trip of your dreams? The free International Video Network Video Catalog can take you there for the price of just a videotape.

You can explore castles, churches, shops, and shrines amidst the charm of Europe's most romantic cities. Wander among streams, rivers, picturesque villages, and the ruins of ancient civilizations in South America. Discover the mysteries of the Orient and marvel at the natural wonders of the U.S., the wildlife of Africa, and the charms of the Caribbean. It's all waiting for you to explore!

To receive this full-color catalog, call (800) 669-4486 or write to International Video Network, 2242 Camino Ramon, San Ramon, CA 94583.

144

13 VIDEOS TO WATCH IF IT DOESN'T HURT WHEN YOU LAUGH

1. **Airplane**. A hilarious spoof of the Airport series—and movies in general. While the jokes don't always work, there are so many of them that this comedy ends up with enough laughs for three movies.

2. **A Night at the Opera**. A classic Marx Brothers' fare as the brothers go en masse to the opera. Need I say more?

3. **Animal House**. Still one of the funniest movies ever made. A wild college fraternity gets placed on "double secret probation" and, of course, blows it with rock 'n' roll, partying, and general craziness.

4. **The Bank Dick**. W.C. Fields is at his best in this laugh-filled comedy. Fields plays a drunkard who becomes a hero. But the story is just an excuse for the many moments of hilarity.

5. **Blazing Saddles**. Mel Brook's raucous spoof of westerns will have you in stitches, if you aren't already.

6. **Ferris Bueller's Day Off**. The charming tale of a high-school legend in his own time who pretends to be ill in order to have a day off from school.

7. **The Goodbye Girl**. Marsha Mason and Richard Dreyfuss are a mismatched pair of New Yorkers forced into becoming roommates in this sparkling Neil Simon classic.

8. **Jay Leno's American Dream**. Comedian and talk show host Jay Leno takes an irreverent look at all that is Americana.

9. **My Man Godfrey**. One of the great screwball comedies of the '30s. William Powell goes from being a hobo to the butler for a wacky family and finds love with Carole Lombard.

10. **Some Like It Hot**. The outlandish story of two men, Jack Lemmon and Tony Curtis, who accidentally witness a gangland slaying and pose as members of an all-girl band. Marilyn Monroe is at her sensual best as the band's singer.

11. **Trading Places.** An uproarious comedy about what happens when an uptight Philadelphia broker (Dan Aykroyd) and a dynamic, street hustler (Eddie Murphy) change places.

12. **What's Up Doc?** This stars Ryan O'Neal as a studio scientist delightfully led astray by a dizzy Barbra Streisand, who keeps forcing herself into his life. The zany final chase through the streets of San Francisco is one of filmdom's best.

13. **When Harry Met Sally**. Can men and women be friends? This film answers the question by laughing all the way as Billy Crystal and Meg Ryan discover their friendship blooming into romance.

145
HEALTHY CURIOSITY

One of the things you can do while lying flat on your back is satisfy your healthy curiosity about the world around you. And two terrific series of books can help. The first series includes the books, *How Do They Do That,* which explores the wonders of today's modern world, and *How Did They Do That,* which takes on mysteries of the far and recent past. These softcover books are $9 each. The second series, called Amazing Explanations, includes three books by David Feldman: *Why Do Clocks Run Clockwise?, Who Put the Butter in the Butterfly?,* and *When Do Fish Sleep?* These softcover books are $9 to $10 each. All these books are available from the Miles Kimball Catalog, (414) 231-4886. Or write to 41 West Eighth Avenue, Oshkosh, WI 54906.

146
BEYOND THE ZOLO ZONE

Imagine a contemporary art version of Mr. Potato Head, and you've got Zolo II, the incredible put-it-together-yourself toy that's never the same twice. (If it is, it's your fault!) Let your imagination go wild with 95 hand-carved, hand-painted wooden pieces that fit together in all kinds of weird ways. Create bizarre animals, wild humanoids, brightly colored creatures from other galaxies, or whatever. This wonderful toy includes curious body forms, colorful connecting sticks, and crazy enders. Packs away in its own pouch and storage drum. $95 from Flax Art and Design, (800) 547-7778. Or write to: Flax Art and Design, 1699 Market St., P.O. Box 7216, San Francisco, CA 94120.

147
NEWS TO YOU

If you're a news buff or talk-show hound, consider sending for the most recent Transcript and Video Index put out by Journal Graphics. It's television "good enough to read" covering shows that include "Good Morning America," "60 Minutes," "20/20," "Nightline," and yes, even "Geraldo." You can order transcripts (and occasionally videos) by checking the comprehensive index in the back. The book lists everything from interviews with actors and actresses to histories of Vietnam. $21.95. You can write to Journal Graphics at 267 Broadway, New York, NY 10007 or call them with a credit card order at (212) 732-8552.

148
VIDEO VOYAGES

In an effort to provide better patient education about preventive care as well as certain medical procedures, some hospitals make a selection of videos available to you on a special TV channel. Topics range from Low Back Pain and Osteoporosis to A Day Away From Stress that offers a welcome 26-minute "vacation" as you follow the steps to relaxation. Screenings are usually held throughout the day, so if you miss one showing, just wait for another one!

149
BECOME A WANDERER

Nothing shrinks the space between the sickroom and the world so much as strolling in a garden or, if walking is impossible, being taken in a wheelchair for a turn outside the hospital. Better still is getting a pass to spend an evening or a weekend at home. Some hospitals are well aware of what you need—a chance to feel the liberty of air, to move about a world that's free of illness, to taste again, however briefly, the life you are forced to leave behind. But even if your hospital is reluctant to make the offer, ask if you can have a pass or suggest to your doctor that he or she issue one.

From *You Can Make It Back: Coping With Serious Illness* by Paul M. Levitt and Elissa S. Guralnick. © 1985. Facts on File Publications, New York, NY $16.95. Currently out of print but still available in many libraries. (212) 683-2244.

150
ADMITTING YOU'RE BORED

If you're stuck for something to read, why not take a few minutes to thoroughly review your admission packet? While not the most scintillating reading in the world, this packet is filled with useful information about everything from walking privileges and chapel services to visiting hours and overnight accommodations for your visitors.

151

FIFTEEN LIGHT EXERCISES

Exercise can relax you, improve your circulation, help with lung expansion, and improve sleep. **Only exercise after getting your doctor's permission, and then start slowly and easily.** The following exercises may be done standing or sitting:

1. Put your hands on the chair arms or in your lap. Pull your shoulder blades together while you breathe in deeply. Relax and slowly breathe out.

2. Shrug your shoulders up and slowly let them down. Then completely relax.

3. Place your hands on the arm or seat of a chair. Push with your hands as if to lift yourself out of the chair. Do not push with your feet.

4. Squeeze your buttocks tightly together. Count to five. Then relax. Don't hold your breath.

5. Put your right hand on your left knee and try to lift your knee up, but press so hard with your hand that you can't relax. Relax. Repeat with your other leg.

6. Lift your arms in front of your face and up over your head, keeping your elbows straight. Do one arm at a time. If this is comfortable, do both together and reach for the ceiling.

7. Lift your arms to the sides and over your head, keeping your elbows straight. Do one arm at a time. If this is comfortable, do both together and reach for the ceiling.

8. Straighten your knees as much as possible, one at a time. And then do both.

9. Press your heels into the floor as if to lift yourself out of your chair.

10. Dig your heels into the floor as if to dig a hole.

11. Place your hands on your shoulders. Make your elbows go in circles.

12. Cross your arms in front of your chest. Then gently bring them back as if to touch your elbows behind your back.

13. Put your hands together in front of your chest. Straighten your fingers as much as possible. Push hands together. Relax.

14. Fold your hands together. Try to pull them apart.

15. Lift your foot slightly off the floor. Point your toes and foot up and down. Then make circles with your foot.

From *I Can Cope* by Judith L. Johnson, R.N., Ph.D. and Linda Klein. © 1994. CHRONIMED Publishing, Minneapolis, MN $9.95. (800) 444-5951.

152
TAPPING INTO BOOKS ON TAPE

For those who have difficulty in reading, holding a book, or keeping attention focused, books on tape are a godsend. Call your local public library to find out if it carries any, or inquire at a well-stocked bookstore in your area. If the bookstore doesn't have what you want, try the following:

Books on Tape, P.O. Box 7900, Newport Beach, CA 92658. Will ship anywhere in the United States. Tapes can be rented or purchased. To order tapes or a catalog, call (800) 626-3333.

Audio Renaissance Tapes, 9110 Sunset Blvd., Suite 200, Los Angeles, CA 90069. (213) 273-9755. A fine selection of interesting and useful tapes, including "Getting Well" by Dr. O. Carl Simonton, as well as others by well-known authors in the field of health and well-being.

Dove Audio, 301 North Canon Drive, Suite 203, Beverly Hills, CA 90210. (800) 328-DOVE or (800) 345-9945. Lots of romances, current best sellers, sci-fi, celebrity biographies, and humor.

Tattered Cover Bookstore, Denver, CO (800) 833-2327. In Colorado, call (800) 821-2896.

From *The Fine Art of Recuperation, A Guide to Surviving and Thriving After Illness, Accident or Surgery* by Regina Sara Ryan. © 1991. Jeremy P. Tarcher Publishing/Putnam Publishing Group, Los Angeles, CA $9.95 (presently out of print). For a complete catalog of Jeremy Tarcher titles, including several related to self-help and the healing process, call (213) 935-9980.

153
DIAL A DISTRACTION

Look in the business section of the white pages of your phone directory under "Dial-a . . ." to find numbers for inspiring and interesting messages. Call and listen.

From *The Fine Art of Recuperation, A Guide to Surviving and Thriving After Illness, Accident or Surgery* by Regina Sara Ryan. © 1991. Jeremy P. Tarcher Publishing/Putnam Publishing Group, Los Angeles, CA $9.95 (presently out of print). For a complete catalog of Jeremy Tarcher titles, including several related to self-help and the healing process, call (213) 935-9980.

154

DARE TO TRY IT

Make a list of 10 activities you always (or almost always) wanted to do but were afraid to try. Consider things you'd like to build, skills you'd like to acquire, knowledge you'd like to gain, creative ideas you've always wanted to express, or social activities you've always wanted to enjoy.

1. _____

2. _____

3. _____

4. _____

5. _____

6. _____

7. _____

8. _____

9. _____

10. _____

Now look over your list and narrow it down to three (or more, if you're ready to go all out with this new project). You might pick the three that seem the least threatening or provide the greatest challenge. It's up to you.

To make your goal a reality, you can use one or all of these five methods:

- Try to learn all by yourself. This involves trial and error, reading the right material, and practicing privately.

- Get an expert to teach you, but you may have to pay or trade for that service. The trade can be something that comes easily for you or involves some skill you already have, such as babysitting, repairing a broken appliance, running an errand, baking cookies, or helping with some task.

- Find a class at a local high school, YMCA or YWCA, university, or community college (evening or day). A benefit here is that you'll have the camaraderie of other students and the structure of a class to support and pace your learning. You'll also have others around to learn from, and if you can control your competitiveness, it can be great fun. Classes are usually not too expensive, especially at state-run facilities.

- Tapes. You can purchase audio- and videotapes for just about any skill. Call your local bookstore, movie rental store, or library.

- Friends or Relatives. You might know a friend or family member who is familiar with the area you wish to learn about. See if the friend is willing to help you on an informal basis.

From *Healing the Body Betrayed: A Self-Paced, Self-Help Guide to Regaining Psychological Control of Your Chronic Illness* by Robert A. Klein, Ph.D. and Marcia Goodman Landau, Ph.D. © 1992. CHRONIMED Publishing, Minneapolis, MN $12.95. (800) 444-5951.

155

MAKING THE BEST OF THE WORST

Compose your own "Bests" or "Worsts" list, including answers to such questions as: What was the worst movie you ever saw? What was your best vacation? Who is your worst-dressed family member? What was the worst meal you ever had on Thanksgiving? And so on.

From *The Fine Art of Recuperation, A Guide to Surviving and Thriving After Illness, Accident or Surgery* by Regina Sara Ryan. © 1991. Jeremy P. Tarcher Publishing/Putnam Publishing Group, Los Angeles, CA $9.95 (presently out of print). For a complete catalog of Jeremy Tarcher titles, including several related to self-help and the healing process, call (213) 935-9980.

156

BANDAIDS FOR BOREDOM

Think of 50 restaurants you've eaten in. Try to remember what you ate, what the interior looked like, and who you were with.

From *The Fine Art of Recuperation, A Guide to Surviving and Thriving After Illness, Accident or Surgery* by Regina Sara Ryan. © 1991. Jeremy P. Tarcher Publishing/Putnam Publishing Group, Los Angeles, CA $9.95 (presently out of print). For a complete catalog of Jeremy Tarcher titles, including several related to self-help and the healing process, call (213) 935-9980.

157

YE OLDE HOUSE OF HOBBIES

Hobbies can be great fun and also lifesavers when you are confined for awhile. If you don't already have a hobby, you probably have at least dreamed at some point of having unlimited time to explore an interest. Make this your chance to follow through on your wish.

Choose a few topics that grab you. Then consider what you can do to begin your exploration. Think of resources close by that you can check. Call your library or local college for references on the topic. Ask family members and friends if they have or can get books on the subject.

antiques	economics
archeology	embroidery
architecture	fishing
art	flower arranging
astronomy	flying
auto maintenance	food preservation
backgammon	foreign languages
basket weaving	furniture design
batik	gardening
biology	gemstones
bonsai	genealogy
bridge	geography
calligraphy	geology
carpentry	history
cartooning	home repair
ceramics	hypnotism
chamber music	indoor plants
chess	investing
coin collecting	jazz
collages	juggling
computers	landscaping
crochet	literature
doll collecting	magic
drawing	math

model building
mythology
needlepoint
opera
origami
painting
philosophy
physics
playwriting
pottery
psychology
quilting

real estate
recipes
robotics
sailing
Shakespeare
stained glass
stamp collecting
travel/adventure
weaving
wine making
yoga

158

KALEIDOSCOPIC ENTERTAINMENT

One of the most pleasant and colorful ways to spend time in bed is by looking through a kaleidoscope. A mini version that fits into your pocket and filled with semi-precious gemstones is available from the Norm Thompson catalog for $35. It comes with its own drawstring pouch, too. Norm Thompson Catalog, (800) 547-1160, 24 hours, 7 days a week. Or write to P.O. Box 3999, Portland, OR 97208.

159
PAINTING OVER BOREDOM

Playing with art can relieve your boredom as well as give you a valuable outlet for self-expression. The Artist's Studio from Norm Thompson is an all-in-one 68-piece kit that lets you create colorful sketches, watercolors, and pastels, while allowing your imagination to truly soar. The collection comes in a sturdy vinyl carrying case to keep the watercolors, pastels, crayons, markers, and tools well organized. $19. Norm Thompson Catalog, (800) 547-1160, 24 hours, 7 days a week. Or write to P.O. Box 3999, Portland, OR 97208.

160

SEVEN GREAT READS—ON TAPE

- *Presumed Innocent* by Scott Thurow. Ten 1 1/2 hour cassettes. Rents for $17.50. Ravaged by obsession, the killer bludgeons a beauty. Only the proof is lacking.

- *The Hunt for Red October* by Tom Clancy. Twelve 1 1/2 hour cassettes. Rents for $18.50. The Russians' most valuable ship, a ballistic missile submarine, defects to the United States. The Soviets try to destroy it—at any cost!

- *The Key to Rebecca* by Ken Follett. Eight 1 1/2 hour cassettes. Rents for $16.50. A suspenseful game of cat and mouse as a British intelligence agent and the woman he loves race against time to catch a murderous spy.

- *The Lonely Silver Rain* by John D. MacDonald. Seven 1 hour cassettes. Rents for $14.50. John D. MacDonald's last Travis McGee novel. McGee gets involved when a custom yacht disappears and a Peruvian debutante dies. The bad guys want McGee dead, too.

- *The Chancellor Manuscript* by Robert Ludlum. Eleven 1 1/2 hour cassettes. Rents for $18.50. Peter Chancellor, a novelist known for political "fictions," makes a fatal discovery in his research: J. Edgar Hoover did not die of natural causes.

- *The Good Mother* by Sue Miller. Nine 1 1/2 hour cassettes. Rents for $17.50. When Anna, recently divorced, finds her dream lover, she has to balance passion for him with love for her daughter. . . a classic dilemma for "the good mother."

- *A Walk Across America* by Peter Jenkins. Seven 1 1/2 hour cassettes. Rents for $16.50. A young man sets out to discover America by walking across it. Along the way, he finds marvelous people and places, and himself.

To order the complete 256-page Books on Tape catalog, call (800) 626-3333. A special offer for new customers includes a 30-day rental plus the catalog for $5.

161

CLAY GRAND PLAY

One of the great unsung stress reducers for people on the mend is playing with a Silly Putty-like substance called Hold It. Manufactured by the Faber-Castell Corporation of Lewisburg, TN, a medium-sized square of Hold It sells for approximately $1.50 and can be found in most art or office supply stores.

Not only is playing with Hold It (or even regular modeling clay) a good tension reliever, it can be used to hang up get well cards, decorations, posters, cheerful thoughts, and anything else you'd like to mount on a flat surface.

162
LOSING YOUR MARBLES

Reexperience marbles in a whole new way! Magnetic Geostax™ marbles let you do things you can't do with ordinary shooters . . . make chains, build pyramids, even play the marble games that NASA astronauts play in zero gravity. An included accessory called Flat Staxs™ lets you build simple or intricate objects. Includes activity booklet. $32 includes 101 marbles and 24 Staxs in a clear plastic bucket with handle and lid. Norm Thompson Catalog, (800) 547-1160, 24 hours, 7 days a week. Or write to P.O. Box 3999, Portland, OR 97208.

163
THE TOP SEVEN HEALING BOOKS

The following books are chosen for their "user-friendly" nature, which is very important for the recuperating person. Most contain both authoritative data and exercises for immediate use.

Anatomy of an Illness. Cousins, N. 1979. W.W. Norton, New York.

Living through Personal Crisis. Stearns, A.K. 1984. Ballantine Books, New York.

Love, Medicine and Miracles: Lessons Learned about Self-Healing from a Surgeon's Experience with Exceptional Patients. Siegel, B., M.D. 1986. Harper & Row, New York.

The Healing Heart: Antidotes to Panic and Helplessness. Cousins, N. 1983. Avon Books, New York.

How Shall I Live? Transforming Surgery or any Health Crisis into Greater Awareness. Moss, R., M.D. 1985. Celestial Arts, Berkeley, CA.

How to Survive the Loss of a Love. Colgrove, M., Bloomfield, H., M.D., and McWilliams, P. 1976. Simon & Schuster, New York. (In this case, you have lost a "love" of some sort if you have endured a health crisis.)

Reconciliations: Inner Peace in an Age of Anxiety. Rubin, T.I., M.D. 1980. Berkley Books, New York.

Wellness Workbook, Travis, J.W., M.D. and Ryan, R.S. 1981, 1988. Ten Speed Press, Berkeley, CA

From *The Fine Art of Recuperation, A Guide to Surviving and Thriving After Illness, Accident or Surgery* by Regina Sara Ryan. © 1991. Jeremy P. Tarcher Publishing/Putnam Publishing Group, Los Angeles, CA $9.95 (presently out of print). For a complete catalog of Jeremy Tarcher titles, including several related to self-help and the healing process, call (213) 935-9980.

164
TRAVEL BY BED

One of the best travel gadget resources in the world is the Magellan's Catalog, (800) 962-4943. It's crammed with things that can help the time go faster, including language learning aids such as cassette tapes, phrase books, and nifty pocket translators that do things like turn any English phrase into Japanese and vice versa.

165
BEDSIDE GARDENING

A good low-maintenance project when you're recuperating is an herb garden featuring your favorite culinary herbs and spices. An herb garden can give you a tremendous sense of peace and hope as you watch it progress. It's easiest if you start with seedlings as opposed to seeds. Just keep your fledgling herbs in a sunny window, and don't forget to water them once or twice a week.

166
BOOKS TO GO

Many books can help you as you heal. Some will help you pass the time, others will assist with specific problems. Still others will be like old friends, just keeping you company. If you can't get to a library or bookstore, you may still be only a phone call away from getting the books you need.

Take advantage of the services offered by many libraries. Often they have a volunteer or homebound program that provides home delivery of the books you want. Call your local branch for information. Bookstores will often ship an order directly to your hospital room or charge your purchase (plus shipping) over the phone. So call and inquire.

From *The Fine Art of Recuperation, A Guide to Surviving and Thriving After Illness, Accident or Surgery* by Regina Sara Ryan. © 1991. Jeremy P. Tarcher Publishing/Putnam Publishing Group, Los Angeles, CA $9.95 (presently out of print). For a complete catalog of Jeremy Tarcher titles, including several related to self-help and the healing process, call (213) 935-9980.

167
MAIL CALL!

If you think now is the time to get more catalogs in your mailbox, a great shortcut is *The Catalog Handbook,* a quarterly publication that lists more than 5,000 catalogs by category and alphabetically. From Aircraft Accessories and Antiques to Woodworking Supplies and Yarns, this handy resource has a catalog for every interest under the sun and tells you how to get on the mailing list. The *Catalog Handbook* is available for $6.95 per copy or $15.95 per year. Call (414) 272-9977 or write to: Enterprise Magazines, 1020 North Broadway, Suite 111, Milwaukee, WI 53202.

168
READING MATTERS

Here are some suggestions for keeping yourself occupied with interesting reading that can hopefully make even the dullest recuperation more interesting:

- Read every book by an author; every spy novel, every romance.
- Read every book in a series, fiction or nonfiction.
- If you like mystery novels, switch to science fiction.
- Read biographies of great people and famous villains.
- Read books that will help your career.
- Read a road atlas. Take a mental vacation—plotting a trip across the west on Route 66, or figuring out how long it would take to drive to Orlando, Florida. Trace the names of towns across the country as the land was gradually settled.
- Reread your old textbooks. Remember how to do geometry? Or borrow your children's or grandchildren's textbooks.
- Read all the sections of the newspaper. Get a different newspaper delivered. Or ask your friends to recycle their newspapers and magazines at your home.
- Subscribe to newsletters published by associations.
- Read recipes or cookbooks.
- Read joke books. Learn knock-knock jokes, elephant jokes, or read cartoon books.

From *Pregnancy Bedrest: A Guide for the Pregnant Woman and Her Family.* by Susan H. Johnston, M.S.W. and Deborah A. Kraut, M.I.L.R. © 1990. Henry Holt, New York, NY $14.95. (212) 886-9200.

169
FANTASY HOTELS

It only costs $15.95 to experience some of the world's most lux-urious hotels and sumptuous resorts when you send for *Resorts and Great Hotels: The International Guide to the World's Best.* It's a delightful inch-thick magazine that lets you travel in style even when you can't get out of bed! For credit card orders, call (805) 687-1422.

170
SENSE-O-RAMA

Check off any of the sensory activities below that you can associate with a happy memory or childhood pleasure. Think of ways you might be able to reexperience that sensation.

Sights
candles
crowds
mirrors
the moon
handsome men/
    pretty women
color
clouds
photos
luxury autos

Sounds
music
pleasant voices
crickets
fizz of a soda can
tuned auto engine
rain
cat purring
ice cubes tinkling
children playing

Smells
food
flowers
gasoline
cut grass
leather
clean sheets
air after rainfall
sweat

Tastes
chocolate
wine
pizza
toasted marshmallows
garlic
Tootsie Roll
peanut butter and jelly
lobster
maple syrup

Touch
velvet
wood
football
kiss
sunlight
massage
clay
warm wool sweater
spouse's/companion's
    arm around you

Kinesthetic
walking
stretching
sex
carnival ride
fishing
riding a bike
sitting quietly
airplane ride

From *Healing the Body Betrayed: A Self-Paced, Self-Help Guide to Regaining Psychological Control of Your Chronic Illness* by Robert A. Klein, Ph.D. and Marcia Goodman Landau, Ph.D. © 1992. CHRONIMED Publishing, Minneapolis, MN $12.95 (800) 444-5951.

GAMES (AND CHALLENGING PUZZLES) GALORE

With special permission of Ken Barry © 1992.

171
COUGH AND A COLD

Inspector Cross didn't have much faith in lie detector tests. But he was so frustrated by the story Martin Haskell told him that he was willing to try anything.

"Honest, Inspector," Haskell had told him with a wide-eyed stare of innocence. "I did everything I could to save Sharon's life! I mean, who would think that a little cough could kill anybody!"

"It was more than a *little* cough," the Inspector said dryly. "According to the medical examiner, your wife had a serious bronchial infection. That's why she choked to death on that chunk of roast beef."

"I thought some red meat would be good for her," the not-too-bereaved husband said sadly. "I thought it would help build up her strength."

"So you cut up the meat and fed it to her yourself."

"I realize now how stupid it was; I should have kept her on a liquid diet. But that doesn't mean I wanted her dead, Inspector! I know that's what you're thinking, but it isn't true!"

He wasn't simply reading the Inspector's mind. Cross had arrived at the Haskell's suburban home armed with neighborhood gossip—that Haskell had a girlfriend, that his wife had been refusing a divorce.

When the polygraph operator was ready, Cross began his questioning. After a few preliminary questions, he asked Haskell if he had done everything he could to save his wife's life.

Haskell's reply was vehement.

"Everything!" he said. "I hit her on the back, but that only made it worse. I tried the Heimlich maneuver, but I just couldn't remember how to do it. I knew she needed a tracheotomy, so I went to the phone book and looked up a surgeon! I called him, but he said he couldn't handle the problem...By the time I got back to the dining room, Sharon was dead."

Later, Cross studied the results of the lie-detector test. They were conclusive. Haskel hadn't told a single lie.

The Inspector was a disappointed man when he started to leave the Haskell house. But then he saw the telephone directory in the front hallway and began turning its pages. Suddenly, he found his answer.

"I'll be back later," he told the honest face of Martin Haskell. "This time, I'll have a warrant for your arrest on negligent homicide."

HOW DID INSPECTOR CROSS KNOW THAT HASKELL HAD HOMICIDE IN MIND?

ACROSS

1. Baseball game souvenirs
5. Overhead trains
8. Trig ratio
12. Jai __
13. "Go, team!"
14. Designer von Furstenberg
15. Kids' PJs
18. Oktoberfest need
19. "Leave __ Beaver"
20. Original
22. Ind. neighbor
23. Atts.' org.
26. Cannonball sound
28. Part of B.P.O.E.
32. Dan Aykroyd film role
35. Inauguration highlight
36. Interoffice communication
37. Dallas sch.
38. Feminine suffix
40. Jeanne d'Arc, for one: Abbr.
42. "Lawrence of Arabia" director
44. Much of Chile
48. Gillespie's subordinate
52. Overexertion result
53. Peanut product
54. Cleveland's lake
55. Way out
56. Memorex competitor
57. Tear apart

DOWN

1. Bounders
2. Considerably
3. Wear a hole in the carpet
4. Kind of protest
5. Do wrong
6. Youngster
7. "He Said, __ Said"
8. Colonist
9. "__ a Name"
10. Off-limits activity
11. USN rank
16. __ a customer
17. Zilch
21. Diet city of 1521
22. Agenda listing
23. Brouhaha
24. Snake with a squeeze
25. Behave
27. "To a Skylark," for instance
29. __ Alamos, NM
30. Kipling book
31. R-V link
33. Moviehouse
34. The bottom line
39. __ cone (summer snack)
41. Bitter- __ (diehard)
42. Plumb crazy
43. Canyon effect
45. Take a chance
46. Ireland's nickname
47. Burpee bit
48. June honoree
49. Deteriorate
50. Kind of gloves
51. Variety

HINT: Polygraph tests can be useful, but the sometimes ambivalent results are inadmissable as evidence. Haskell volunteered to take the test because he simply wanted Inspector Cross off his back. He knew the best way was to

```
—  —  —  —   —  —  —   —  —  —
A  B  C  D   E  F  G   H  I  J

—  —  —  —   —  —   —  —  —  —
K  L  M  N   O  P   Q   R  S  T  U  V
```

HOW TO PLAY: To fill in the five missing words in the Hint, first complete the crossword above. Then, transfer the letters contained in the squares marked A through V into the corresponding blanks in the Hint. *Solution on pg. 262.*

From *Inspector Cross Twenty Unique Crossword Capers & Mystery Word Teasers, Volume I* by Stanley Newman. Lombard Marketing, $12.95. (800) 874-6556. Volume II is also available from the same company.

172
A SHOT IN THE ARM

Inspector Cross liked the Swordfish Bar and Grill. It was a cozy, wood paneled place around the corner from the police station. What he liked best was the fact that the bartender never blinked an eye when he ordered his customary glass of milk. The Inspector never drank on duty – or off.

Sergeant Kingsley didn't share the Inspector's affection for the Swordfish, and especially not for the bartender.

"They call him'Doc,' you know," the Sergeant grumbled. "And he's always handing out free advice."

"That's a bartender's sacred duty," Cross smiled. "Where else can a man go when he has troubles at home?"

"Sometimes he gives medical advice, too. That's how he got his nickname."

"I've heard him advise some of our men," Cross said. "He told them to eat more fruit and less doughnuts."

"Okay, I know you think it's funny," Kingsley said. "But one of these day, that guy is going to go too far."

The Inspector didn't recall the conversation until a month later, when a triumphant Sergeant Kingsley bustled into his office.

"Did you know your friend Doc keeps a gun under the bar?"

"Of course," Cross said. "I helped him get it registered. It's just for protection."

"Well, he just pulled that gun, but it wasn't on a holdup man! It was a legitimate customer!"

"What?" Cross said in surprise.

"That's what a pal of mine just told me. He was having a beer at the Swordfish when a man came in and asked for a glass of water. Instead of giving it to him, Doc pulled out a gun and stuck it in his face!"

"There's got to be some mistake."

"Maybe your friend was sore because the guy didn't ask for a shot of whiskey!"

The Inspector insisted on seeing Kingsley's beer-drinking pal, who solemnly swore to the event he witnessed.

"I wasn't real close to the bar," he admitted. "But I did hear the guy ask for the water, and I saw Doc pull that gun!"

"Then what happened?"

"That was the peculiar part. The guy said 'thanks' and then turned and walked out."

When Inspector Cross began to chuckle, the Sergeant became indignant. "I think we ought to haul this guy Doc in for questioning!"

"There's no need for that," Cross said. "I already know what happened."

HOW DID INSPECTOR CROSS EXPLAIN THE ACTIONS OF DOC THE BARTENDER?

HINT: Doc had never seen the man before, so there was no personal grudge involved. And the gun wasn't loaded, so there was no actual danger to the customer. Inspector Cross is a fine judge of character, and he knew Doc's intentions were good. Now_____.

HOW TO PLAY: You'll use the diagram on the following page to fill in the rest of the Hint. First, find and circle the names of 19 famous "Doctors" of fact or fiction. Answers all read in a straight line, either forward, backward, up, down, or diagonally. Some answers may overlap and some letters may be used more than once. As an extra hint, all answers are at least three letters long. When you've circled all 19 answers, the unused letters, reading from left to right, from top to bottom, will spell the missing words. *Solution on pg. 263.*

```
F  H  C  I  L  M  I  E  H  F  Y  I
R  R  G  U  E  L  T  T  I  L  O  D
E  F  A  U  S  T  U  S  P  R  C  E
U  O  O  N  K  L  A  S  P  U  C  T
D  G  K  W  K  W  H  O  O  H  M  A
D  A  C  L  L  E  W  K  C  A  L  B
E  V  O  L  E  G  N  A  R  T  S  T
M  I  P  T  H  A  T  S  A  I  N  T
E  H  S  C  H  W  E  I  T  Z  E  R
N  Z  E  H  T  U  R  N  E  E  T  I
T  W  A  T  S  O  N  O  S  N  I  W
O  A  S  S  Y  E  K  A  B  E  D  N
```

From *Inspector Cross Twenty Unique Crossword Capers & Mystery Word Teasers, Volume I* by Stanley Newman. Lombard Marketing $12.95. (800) 874-6556. Volume II is also available from the same company.

173
PRESCRIPTION FOR MURDER

Inspector Cross thought he would enjoy his dinner date with Joyce, a nurse he met while investigating the death of her employer. The case was routine; the doctor had died in a traffic accident. But there was nothing routine about Joyce. She was blonde and beautiful.

Unfortunately, she had a roommate. Vicki had a tendency to talk too much. Cross sighed when Vicki invited herself along.

The Inspector barely listened to the coversation, until Vicki mentioned the Man with the Green Hat. The Sherlockian phrase perked his interest.

"It was really weird," Vicki said. "I mean that he showed up both times. When your doctor had his accident *and* when my doctor had his coronary."

"It *was* just a coincidence," Joyce said to the Inspector. "He came into our offices the day after the doctor died to make an appoinment for his wife. He seemed so disappointed, and he hung around the office for almost an hour. I had to ask him to leave."

"Then I saw him," Vicki said. "He came in while we were emptying out poor Dr. Rosen's office. He didn't realize Rosen had died two days ago."

Cross had heard of stranger coincidences. But then Joyce said, "Of course, we're not sure it was the same man who tried to see Dr. Mead . . . ."

"Mead?" the Inspector said. "I just saw his obituary last week!"

"His office is in the same building," Vicki said. "And I could swear I saw the green hat again. It gives you the creeps, doesn't it? Visting the offices of dead doctors?"

The next morning, Inspector Cross did just that. He spoke to Dr. Mead's nurse, who told him there *was* a man with a green hat: a nervous man with an invalid wife. And she *did* get his name. Cross was grateful.

The man's name was Felton, and he couldn't understand the police interest. He was just trying to make a medical appointment, he protested. His wife had been sick for months.

Inspector Cross suggested, "Is it possible you've gotten a bit tired of that sick wife? And are trying to kill her?"

There was a cry from the bedroom, and the Inspector rushed inside. Within fifteen minutes, there was an ambulance for Mrs. Felton – and a police vehicle for Mr. Felton.

WHAT WAS FELTON AFTER IN THE OFFICES OF THE DEAD DOCTORS? WHY DID THE INSPECTOR SUSPECT A MURDER PLOT

ACROSS

1. Affectations
5. Sheltered spot
9. Disordered situation
12. Predetermine the outcome
15. Small band
16. Malevolent
17. Provide with weaponry
18. Ram remark
19. Intimately associated
21. HINTWORD #1
23. Tennis term
24. Pretense
26. "We _the World"
27. HINTWORD #2
30. Roger Rabbit, for one
32. HINTWORD #3
36. Historical period
37. When the French fry
41. "Betsy's Wedding" star
43. Edmond O'Brien classic film
44. Taj Mahal town
46. Facilitate
48. HINTWORD #4
50. High schooler
51. Necks of the woods
53. Loquacious
54. Makeup accessory
58. New car option
61. Thompson of fiction
62. Early communications
66. Kitchen devices
69. Ocean liner?
70. Dinner course

DOWN

1. Close by
2. Tax-deferred acct.
3. ___ Tin Tin
4. Fast-food drinks
5. Honeycomb unit
6. Ab _(from the beginning)
7. "_Zapata!"
8. Vote in
9. Destroy, arcade-style
10. Florida city
11. General Bradley
12. Slugger's stat
13. Author Fleming
14. Comedian's bit
20. Happiness
22. Evergreen variety
25. One _customer
27. Cleverly done
28. Hankering
29. Hard to find
31. Antiquated
33 Admired one
34. Road sight
35. Elementary
38. "_she blows"
39. Architect Saarinen
40. Bunches
42. Play beginning
45. Keep _ (watch)
47. Dads
49. Narratives
52. Closed car
55. Cook up
56. "About a Quarter to _"

ACROSS *(Cont.)*

71. Review unfavorably
72. Moistens
74. Have to have
76. Hockey great Bobby
77. Mideast airline
79. It's held for questioning
81. Vacuous
83. — de cologne
85. Favorite
87. Buddy, in Brittany
88. HINTWORD #5
92. Talk too much
97. Recipe phrase
98. Uncommon sense
99. Peruse
100. "__ Rhythm"
101. Monkey suit, for short
102. Eye sore
103. African snakes
104. Explorer Hernando De____

DOWN *(Cont.)*

57. Give up
58. Manage somehow
59. Whitish gem
60. Actress Olin
63. Henhouse
64. "Broadcast News" star
65. Grand Ole ____
67. Petition
68. R-V filler
73. Tea taste
75. Floor model
78. Maui souvenir
80. Referee, informally
82. Short skirts
84. Poker pair
86. Links areas
87. Does sums
88. Bran source
89. Winter bug
90. Send documents by phone
91. Secret agent
93. Forty winks
94. Conceit
95. Drunkard
96. Keep an __ the ground

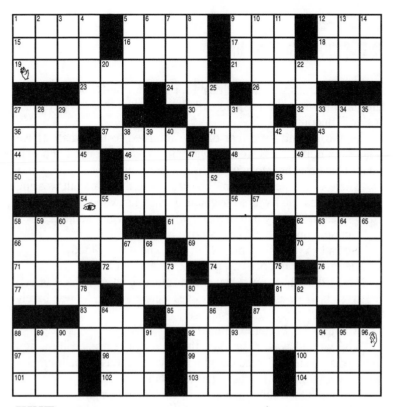

HINT: Mr. Felton was tired of $\overline{\text{Hintword #1}}$ $\overline{\text{Hintword #2}}$ to his $\overline{\text{Hintword #3}}$. But he didn't want suspicion to fall on him if she passed away. He thought of a foolproof scheme, but it required something found only in $\overline{\text{Hintword #4}}$ $\overline{\text{Hintword #5}}$ – preferably deceased ones.

HOW TO PLAY: Five Hintwords are missing from the Hint. These Hintwords will be found by solving the crossword above. As an added challenge, the three "body parts" drawn in the answer diagram are to be used as part of their respective answers wherever they appear. *Solution on pg. 264.*

From *Inspector Cross Twenty Unique Crossword Capers & Mystery Word Teasers, Volume I* by Stanley Newman. Lombard Marketing $12.95. (800) 874-6556. Volume II is also available from the same company.

174.
INFECTIOUS CONDITION

Inspector Cross waited anxiously for a report on Dr. Porter's condition. But when the hospital called, he learned that the physician was still unconscious

For the second time that day, he returned to the small office where his nurse, Miss Yerkes, was still looking red-eyed and nervous. This time, her story was a little more coherent.

"There were three of them," she said, "and they were all wearing Halloween masks. I was so frightened when I saw them that I started to scream. That's when one of them pointed a gun at me..."

"But only one of them appeared to be wounded?"

"He had a crude sling on his left arm, and it was bloody."

The Inspector nodded. "A gunshot wound, of course."

"Yes, I thought it must have been infected, because he was acting so sick. He was sniffling, his eyes were running, he was barely able to walk."

"And then Dr. Porter examined him."

"The wound wasn't serious; the bullet only grazed him, and there was no sign of infecton. Obviously, there was something else wrong with him. Dr. Porter suggested a hospital..."

"I'm sure that didn't go over well," Cross said wryly.

"The other two got *very* upset at that idea! They didn't want to hang around anymore, so they gave the sick man a gun and told him he was on his own. Then they ran out."

"It was then that Dr. Porter tried to reach the police?"

"Yes! I was putting on a fresh dressing, when the Doctor ran for the phone. The man struck him on the back of the head with his pistol, and left...Oh, if only I could describe them!" she said.

The Inspector said, "You're not the only one. A dozen people at the First Federal Bank wish they could do the same thing."

He was gratified when he called the hospital once more and learned that the doctor had regained consciousness and could talk to him for a few moments. He was even more gratified when Porter told him about the sick man's condition. When he hung up, Cross turned to the nurse and said, "Maybe we *can* identify them, Miss Yerkes."

"But how? They were all masked. They never took their masks off for one second!"

HOW DID INSPECTOR CROSS IDENTIFY THE BANDITS? SOLVE THE PUZZLE AND SEE.

A. Occupational equipment (4 wds.) ....

....56 9 98 127 161 88 20 148 112 163 38 67 203 234 103

B. Cocktail (2 wds.) ....

.....................172 85 16 47 233 68 41 133 167 195 145 185 33 120 179 206

C. Friend of the above? (full name) ....

....54 135 182 142 176 62 7 231 116 213 94

D. Farragut's command (3 wds.) ....

..................28 60 158 191 82 109 129 238 225 13 35 101 137 207 149 170

E. City in Wisconsin

....122 164 92 198 15 131 30

F. "It stuck in my–" ....

....96 232 79 63

G. Playground equipment ....

....147 93 3 171 168 19 193 58 181 215 146 227 34

H. "It's all a matter –"..

....153 222 177 119 72 8 48

I. Agatha's murder victim ....

....150 51 111 36 138 156 115 205 99 196 5 107

J. Australia (2 wds.) ....

....90 200 78 61 22 117 186 136 40

K. Bug killers ....

....76 230 25 44 220 105 125 132 187 12 210 124

L. "He jests at scars that never felt –" (2 wrds.)............................

....83 154 95 139 204 100

M. Masochists (3 wds.) ....

....53 89 190 65 102 237 155 11 218 39 49

....14 74 166 110 130 184 6 46 128 77

N. Proved culpable ....
....$\overline{59}$ $\overline{144}$ $\overline{192}$ $\overline{113}$ $\overline{71}$ $\overline{24}$

O. Celestial spheres...
....$\overline{197}$ $\overline{180}$ $\overline{208}$ $\overline{157}$

P. Snobbish..
....$\overline{4}$ $\overline{29}$ $\overline{223}$ $\overline{50}$ $\overline{151}$ $\overline{123}$ $\overline{236}$

Q. Followed..
....$\overline{175}$ $\overline{23}$ $\overline{235}$ $\overline{229}$ $\overline{31}$ $\overline{86}$

R. No-nonsense footwear (2 wds.) ....
...............................$\overline{212}$ $\overline{18}$ $\overline{152}$ $\overline{239}$ $\overline{57}$ $\overline{202}$ $\overline{126}$ $\overline{106}$ $\overline{174}$ $\overline{216}$ $\overline{228}$ $\overline{221}$ $\overline{169}$

S. Pioneering TV sitcom (4 wds.) ....
.........................$\overline{108}$ $\overline{134}$ $\overline{162}$ $\overline{27}$ $\overline{81}$ $\overline{91}$ $\overline{2}$ $\overline{69}$ $\overline{45}$ $\overline{217}$ $\overline{188}$ $\overline{214}$ $\overline{143}$ $\overline{194}$

T. Famous Puritan, son of Increase (full name) ....
....$\overline{87}$ $\overline{21}$ $\overline{118}$ $\overline{97}$ $\overline{183}$ $\overline{52}$ $\overline{10}$ $\overline{219}$ $\overline{75}$ $\overline{178}$ $\overline{42}$ $\overline{211}$

U. "– buggy bumpers," radio announcer test phrase (2 wds.)
....$\overline{43}$ $\overline{165}$ $\overline{140}$ $\overline{73}$ $\overline{159}$ $\overline{201}$ $\overline{209}$ $\overline{160}$ $\overline{84}$ $\overline{114}$

V. Type variation ....
....$\overline{121}$ $\overline{1}$ $\overline{64}$ $\overline{224}$ $\overline{32}$ $\overline{104}$ $\overline{80}$

W. Clinic; Irish county; sandwich spread ....
....$\overline{189}$ $\overline{26}$ $\overline{70}$ $\overline{173}$

X. Personal belongings ....
....$\overline{66}$ $\overline{199}$ $\overline{226}$ $\overline{141}$ $\overline{37}$ $\overline{17}$ $\overline{55}$

HOW TO PLAY: First read the mystery story and see if you
know the answer. Then guess the words defined on this and the
previous page and write them in. Transfer each letter to the
square with the same number. The first letters of the defined
words will give you the subtitle to the story. The finished puzzle
will give you the last paragraph of the story – and the solution to
the mystery. *Solution on pg. 265.*

From *Inspector Cross Twenty Unique Crossword Capers & Mystery Word Teasers, Volume I* by Stanley Newman. Lombard Marketing $12.95. (800) 874-6556. Volume II is also available from the same company.

175
PAY THROUGH THE NOSE

Inspector Cross wasn't comfortable in the offices of Dr. Hubert Strang – he kept imagining that the doctor was staring at his nose.

It may not have been an ideal nose, but the Inspector was attached to it, and Dr. Strang's business was changing noses, eyes, chins, and other features. Strang was a cosmetic surgeon, and at the moment a very agitated one.

"You can't imagine what an ordeal I've been through!" he said. "I've been a virtual prisoner in my own clinic!"

"Just tell me exactly how it happened," Cross said soothingly. "Did you recognize 'Big Nose' Tommy Burke when he came to see you?"

"How could I help it? His face has been plastered all over the media since that armored car robbery! To tell you the truth, when I saw him on TV, I couldn't help thinking what a great patient he would make."

"But you never expected he'd walk in and demand an operation–at the point of a .45."

Strang shuddered at the memory. "He made me dismiss both my nurse and receptionist without telling them the real reason. I had to perform the operation without assistance – except for that goon friend of his. And the only instrument that guy handled was a gun!"

"Of course he couldn't let you leave the place until his face was healed," Inspector Cross said. "But what I need to know is – was the operation successful?"

"I've never done better work," the Doctor said. "Nobody will ever call him 'Big Nose' Burke again."

"And more important, he won't be so recognizable again."

"I usually take before-and-after pictures of my patients, but of course he wouldn't allow that in this case. But I can tell you this much – his own mother wouldn't recognize him."

Inspector Cross grunted. "Assuming his mother lives in South America. You're sure that's where he's headed?"

"I ought to know," Strang said. "He made me drive him to the airport and see him into the South American Airlines terminal…He's gotten away with millions! And all because I'm so darned good." Dr. Strang didn't seem entirely displeased.

To his surprise, Inspector Cross smiled. "Don't worry about it, Doctor. I can safely predict that 'Big Nose' – or 'Little Nose' – will be safely in our custody within twenty-four hours!" And once again, the Inspector was right.

WHY WAS INSPECTOR CROSS SO SURE OF THE CAPTURE OF 'BIG NOSE' BURKE?

ACROSS

1. It holds water
5. Dutch treat
9. Did in, old-style
13. Have it out
19. Actress McClurg
20. Clock
21. Window glass
22. Titania's spouse
23. PART 1 OF HINT
26. __oneself (kept occupied)
27. Jackie's second
28. Legal attachment
29. Felt poorly
30. Ski lifts
31. Soup ingredients
33. Agitate
34. Oxford, for instance
37. Caesar's greeting
38. Ship's crewman
40. Devour
44. "The Sleeping Prophet"
47. Throat-culture finding
48. Beef
49. Old West
50. Latin I verb
51. Pitcher's place
52. "I Fall to Pieces" singer
53. Angry mood
54. $1,000,000 for short
55. "Why?"
56. Where the money goes
57. Wedding-chapel inventory
58. Historical period
59. Overwhelming impression
60. Finish line
62. "A Doll's House" playwright
65. PART 2 OF HINT
68. "No, __thousand times no!"

DOWN

1. Open to bribery
2. Just love
3. Kind of strike
4. Snakelike fish
5. Prima ballerina
6. Flood preventers
7. Ugandan exile
8. What boys will be
9. Divorce
10. Send away
11. Rubber stamp accessory
12. Got ready to drive
13. Denver, but not Houston
14. __Dhabi
15. Tried out
16. Threesome
17. Early theater magnate
18. They may split
24. Loon-egg color
25. __up (filled one's tank)
32. Diplomat's need
34. Kicker's target
35. "Cancel My Reservation" star
36. Be in the red
38. Air-conditioner units
39. "Believe It__!"
40. Leonard Maltin's occupation
41. Atlanta arena
42. Trumpet effect
43. NBA team
44. Dove rival
45. Buddy, in Barcelona
46. Pres. Buch's alma mater
47. "And you do it __!"
48. Day-__(kind of paint)
51. Lawn need
52. Weather forecast
53. Dispatch

ACROSS *(Cont.)*

69. PART 3 OF HINT
73. Some nobility
74. Author Ephron
76. Never, in Nuremburg
77. Spectator's shout
78. Distend
81. Follow
83. Woody Woodpecker's creator
85. Bauxite, e.g.
86. Sgt. Friday's employer
87. Deteriorate
89. Works at
90. Gives a bad review
91. One of California's Santas
92. Take the honey and run
93. "Roger & Me" city
94. Thickly packed
95. Dunderheads
97. Bias
98. Boom-bah preceder
99. Cow pastures
100. __above the rest
101. Highway inconveniences
105. Rose Mary Murphy's hubby
108. Play the ham
109. "In the __ of the Night"
110. Shemp's brother
111. Caledonian cloth
114. END OF HINT
117. Ancient fortune-teller
118. Fouls up
119. Piece of merchandise
120. Pinochle combo
121. Fit together
122. Remainder
123. Chopped down
124. Victim

DOWN *(Cont.)*

55. Contends with
56. Bobbin
57. "The Mexican Spitfire"
61. The musical of "Tomorrow"
63. Easter hat
64. Civil complaints
66. Scanned
67. Camera settings
70. Sound annoyed
71. Brings home
72. "Some of __Days"
75. Exhausted
78. Tasteless
79. Turner of films
80. Whitish gem
82. Lime drink
84. "__She Sweet?"
87. Director Kazan
88. Decays
89. Typewriter part
90. Mexican money
92. Lamb's mom
93. Galway is one
94. "Me too!"
96. Chase detective
97. Cleans thoroughly
98. Scorched
100. Love, Italian style
101. Raison __
102. "Burnt" color
103. Esther of "Good Times"
104. Run-down
105. Energy source
106. Unadorned
107. Tax-deferred accounts
108. Staring one
109. Barnum specialty
112. British brew
113. Actor Beatty
115. American competitor
116. He cleans his plate

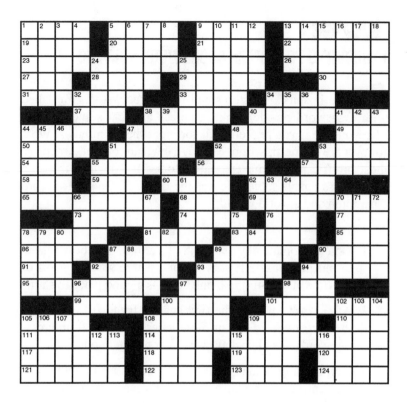

HINT: The doctor knew his stuff, and 'Big Nose' Burke's famous face was completely unrecongnizable. But there are some circumstances when:

_____

Part #1 of Hint

_____

Part #2 of Hint

_____

Part # 3 of Hint

HOW TO PLAY: The missing part of the Hint will be found by completing the crossword above. *Solution on pg. 266.*

From *Inspector Cross Twenty Unique Crossword Capers & Mystery Word Teasers, Volume I* by Stanley Newman. Lombard Marketing $12.95. (800) 874-6556. Volume II is also available from the same company.

176
10 SECRETS TO BETTER CROSSWORD SOLVING

Because hospital gift stores and regular bookstores are filled with crossword puzzle books, chances are that someone may give you one if you're feeling ill for more than 5 minutes. What follows are inside tips from Stanley Newman, one of America's most prolific puzzle makers and editors. Mr. Newman is also a world-class puzzle solver. He was the first U.S. Open Crossword Champion and a world record.

1. Don't automatically start with 1 Across. The best answer to put in a puzzle first is the one you're sure of. Most of the time, a "fill-in-the-blank" clue is a good place to start.

2. After you've written the first answer, try to fill in answers that already have one or more letters filled in from crossing words. It's almost always easier to figure out.

3. Don't "jump around," filling in answers all over the puzzle. Your solving will be easier and faster if you concentrate on one area of the puzzle at a time. If you're unable to fill in any answers in the area you're working in, look for a "fill-in-the-blank" clue in a nearby section of the puzzle and try to link up with the area you were working on before.

4. If you become "hopelessly stuck," it's okay to take a peek at the answers for a little help. Some people think it's "cheating," but it's perfectly all right. You won't get stuck on the same clues next time if you learn them now.

5. When you're done, check your answers with the printed solution. You'd be surprised how often an answer you thought was right isn't.

6. Don't solve puzzles in pen unless you never make mistakes. If you want to impress onlookers, use an erasable pen.

7. Be choosey about which crosswords you do. Experts agree that the "best" crosswords are those that contain a broad spectrum of facts (not just dictionary definitions), have lively language, make use of humor and wordplay, and avoid obscure words.

8. Part of the fun of crossword solving comes from getting to know the personalities of the people that create them. For this reason, you should avoid puzzles (in magazines, books, and newspapers) where the author's name is not given.

9. Try to do puzzles that are slightly above your current level of expertise. It's no great accomplishment to fill in a puzzle as fast as you can write if you're not learning anything in the process.

10. Be sure to look up all unfamiliar words and references. This may involve more than your unabridged dictionary, since today's best puzzles use a wide variety of information. But your vocabulary and knowledge base will increase steadily as a result, and that's the best way to improve your solving skill.

From *Inspector Cross Twenty Unique Crossword Capers & Mystery Word Teasers, Volume I* by Stanley Newman. Lombard Marketing $12.95. (800) 874-6556. Volume II is also available from the same company.

177
CROSSWORD COMPUTER

Now you can find the crossword answer that's been stumping you with some electronic help. An entire crossword dictionary is packed into this palm-sized automatic solver. Just enter the unsolved fragment shown on your puzzle and Franklin's Crosswords Puzzle Solver offers you several possible solutions. Even use it to finish phrases, to solve word jumbles, or play Scrabble. Contains 250,000 words from Merriam Webster and includes countries, capitals, geographic names, languages and much more. Runs on one lithium battery, which is included. $49 from Attitudes (800) 525-2468, 24 hours a day. Or write to: Attitudes, P.O. Box 61148, Sunnyvale, CA 94088-1148.

178
PUZZLING NEWSLETTERS

If you're a true crossword fanatic, you may want to invest in two newsletters for puzzle lovers:

TOUGH PUZZLES/$25 for 6 issues
American Crossword Federation
Box 69
Massapequa Park, NY 11762
(516) 795-8823

PUZZLELETTER/$12 year
Dartnell Cambridge Associates
164 Canal St.
Boston, MA 02114
(617) 723-5969

179

PUTTING ALL THE PIECES TOGETHER

The first-ever three dimensional jigsaw puzzle lets you build a Bavarian castle a king would envy! This puzzle has jigsaw-shaped pieces, but like a model, it is constructed rather than "put together." And that construction process will challenge the ingenuity and spatial abilities of the most experienced puzzle expert. The pieces are backed with a thin layer of foam that provides stability. 13" x 22" x 16" when completed and quite a conversation piece. $39. Norm Thompson Catalog, (800) 547-1160, 24 hours, 7 days a week. Or write to: P.O. Box 3999, Portland, OR 97208.

180
DOMINO EFFECT

Ever tried indoor racing? Domino racing, that is. You can race against yourself by setting up 500 blank dominos in a snake-like pattern, up and over a wooden bridge, which is thoughtfully included. The first domino starts a chain reaction while the last one rings a special ringing bell. Or divide the set into two for a race. Dominos come in four colors. $55.90. To order contact Hearth Song, Mail Processing Center, 6519 Galena Road, Peoria, IL 61614. (800) 325-2502.

Reprinted with permission from *Bottom Line Personal,* 330 W. 42nd St., New York, NY 10036. 24 issues per year/$49 per year or $4 per issue. (800) 274-5611.

181

ROBOTS THAT KEEP YOU FROM GOING BUGGY

Here's your chance to be the center of attention with robotic bugs no exterminator will want to eliminate! Build them from a handy kit that contains everything you need except the batteries. The Spider robot "walks" on six legs and emits an infrared beam to detect and avoid obstacles in its path. The Manta robot has a touch/sound sensor. If it comes in contact with an object or hears a loud noise, it reverses and takes a new course. Lots of fun. Spider, $69; Manta, $39. Norm Thompson Catalog, (800) 547-1160, 24 hours, 7 days a week. Or write to: P.O. Box 3999, Portland, OR 97208.

182
LOGICAL RECOVERY

The *Fantastic Book of Logic Puzzles* will spark your imagination, sharpen your thinking, and make the time pass more quickly. This book contains 70 illustrated puzzles that need a plan of attack and logic to solve them. Each chapter starts with easy puzzles and works up to tougher ones. Solutions are provided in case you're totally baffled. Softcover, $4.95 from the Miles Kimball Catalog, (414) 231-4886. Or write to: 41 West Eighth Avenue, Oshkosh, WI 54906.

183
FAST SHUFFLE

If you like card games, but your hands aren't cooperating with shuffling the deck, the Automatic Card Shuffler may offer one solution. This battery-operated shuffler professionally shuffles one or two decks with just a press of a button. Operates on two C cell batteries, which are not included. $10.98 from the Miles Kimball Catalog, (414) 231-4886. Or write to: 41 West Eighth Avenue, Oshkosh, WI 54906.

184

FAN DANCE

For baseball fanatics on the mend, Franklin's pocket-sized Baseball Encyclopedia computer contains more than 620,000 batting statistics, 270,000 pitching statistics, plus personal information for every player in the history of Major League Baseball. Find complete data for every American and National League team, World Series, and major player awards since 1876. Compare players' performances, evaluate trades, and answer trivia questions. Use the powerful database commands to compile your own best/worst or oldest/youngest lists in virtually any category. Includes two lithium batteries. $79 from Solutions, (800) 342-9988. 24 hours a day. Or write to: Solutions, Dept. P.O. Box 6878, Portland, OR 97228.

185
HIGH STAKES ACTION

Here's your chance to win up to $1 million in thrilling (but imaginary) profits with an exciting computer poker game. Play 5-card draw poker against the crafty and animated dealer. Play is fully realistic: you can draw, bet (up to $100,000 at a time—but not exceeding chips in your hand), raise, drop, and call. Two skill levels let you play with all the dealer's cards hidden or two exposed. Watch the dealer's expression change when you win (or lose a big pot). Enjoy the game with fun sound effects or play in silence. Runs on two batteries, which are included. $52 from Attitudes (800) 525-2468, 24 hours a day. Or write to: Attitudes, P.O. Box 61148, Sunnyvale, CA 94088-1148.

186
MOVES OF THE MASTERS

W hether you're at home or in the hospital, you can play against a chess master anytime, day or night. Chesster is an interactive chess game that talks to you during play, comments (often humorously) on your moves, and offers sound advice to improve your ability. With 25 skill levels from beginner to advanced, you can play against a partner of equal ability or step up to a more competitive level. The U.S. Chess Federation gives Chesster a rating of 2100, which is higher than the skill level of 95% of the world's players. So be prepared! Chesster offers plenty of challenge for even the most experienced players. Uses four AA batteries, which are not included. $249 from The World's Greatest Gaming Catalog, (800) 345-7017. Or write to: The World's Greatest Gaming Catalog, John Patrick Productions, 514 Milburn Avenue, P.O. Box 289, Short Hills, NJ 07078.

187

BRIDGE OVER TROUBLED WATERS

The Pro Bridge 500 computer bridge player has a powerful 128K program with levels to challenge anyone from beginner to the most experienced club player. It can also coach you—offering hints and suggestions, even allowing take back of a bid or card. It can review a game with all hands on view, so you can see how players interact. Or you can watch the computer play itself, and pick up ideas on how to improve your game. Pro Bridge plays all major bridge systems and allows for five major bidding systems. A great traveler, with a compact laptop design. $395 (AC adapter $16 extra) from Attitudes (800) 525-2468, 24 hours a day. Or write to: Attitudes, P.O. Box 61148, Sunnyvale, CA 94088-1148.

188
FAST REFLEX ACTION

Hit Klok, Matchmaker, and Go Mental may not sound like interesting ways to spend your time recuperating, but once you play them, you'll be hooked! These three fascinating electronic games test your concentration and your reflexes. Try to keep up with flashing numbers or rapidly expanding blocks and lines by hitting buttons. As you improve, the devilish computer speeds up. Each game also features a built-in clock with alarm. $20 each from Attitudes (800) 525-2468, 24 hours a day. Or write to: Attitudes, P.O. Box 61148, Sunnyvale, CA 94088-1148.

189

WELL MATCHED IN BACKGAMMON

Backgammon is one of the great one-on-one gambling games of all time, requiring knowledge of the odds, an acute sense of strategy and timing, and psychological cunning. And there's no better way to learn the game than with Electronic Backgammon Challenger. You'll learn all the moves, the different styles of play, when to double and why, when to take, and when to drop. Eight selectable skills levels. $79 from The World's Greatest Gaming Catalog, (800) 345-7017. Or write to: The World's Greatest Gaming Catalog, John Patrick Productions, 514 Milburn Avenue, P.O. Box 289, Short Hills, NJ 07078.

190
CASINO BUSTER

Short of a visit to Las Vegas or Atlantic City, there's no better way to practice your blackjack skills than with the handheld Pro Blackjack Game from Saitek. You can start a game anytime, play with up to four players and six decks of cards, bet from $10 to $1,000, and learn valuable card-counting skills if you're interested. Includes a hint function that offers advice on when to hit, stand, split, or double down, according to Las Vegas rules. 200 hours of fun on one lithium battery. $52 from Attitudes (800) 525-2468, 24 hours a day. Or write to: Attitudes, P.O. Box 61148, Sunnyvale, CA 94088-1148.

191
GAMBLER'S SECRET

If you consider yourself a gambler, and you'd enjoy playing everything from hand-held poker games to getting expert instruction in casino action and horse racing while you're recuperating, call for a free copy of The World's Greatest Gaming Catalog, (800) 345-7017.

192
NOTEWORTHY THOUGHTS

If you just don't feel like writing your thoughts down, a Sony Notetaker mini-recorder can let you record up to 2 hours of ideas, thoughts, and reminders without putting pen to paper. The voice activated recording (VAR) capability starts the recorder only when you speak so you don't waste tape while you're thinking. Also comes with ingenious earphone for playback. 3.5 ounces and measures just 2.75" x 2.6" x 7.5". Runs for 5 hours on a single AAA battery, not included. $299. From the Herrington Catalog, (800) 622-5221. Or write to: Herrington, 3 Symmes Drive, Londonderry, NH 03053.

GADGETS AND GIZMOS

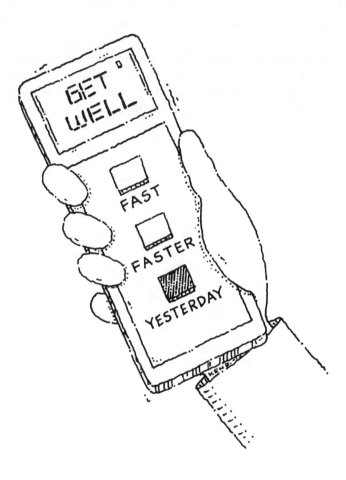

With special permission of Ken Barry © 1992

193
MINIMUM SIZE, MAXIMUM FUN

- **Pocket-Sized TV.** About the size and thickness of two bill-folds—3 3/16 x 1 7/8 x 5 7/16 inches. Has a 2.2-inch color LCD screen. Operates on four AA batteries. Model TV-470 from Casio is $199.95.

- **Palm-Sized Camcorder.** 4 3/8 x 4 1/4 x 7 1/4 inches. Weighs less than 2 pounds without batteries. Includes features found on much larger units—built-in stereo microphone, lux light sensitivity, 8:1 power zoom, fader and shutter speeds up to 1/4000 of a second. Model R-86 Super from Ricoh is $1,599.

- **Tiny CD Player.** About the size of two of the slim plastic cases used to hold compact discs. A batter-saving feature shuts the unit off if it's left in the stop or pause mode for 5 minutes. Includes two rechargeable batteries, an AC adapter/charger, headphones, and a soft carrying case. Model SL-XP7000 from Technics is $299.95.

- **Personal "Walkman" Stereo.** Comes with all the bells and whistles. About the size of a deck of cards. AM/FM and cassette. Quartz digital tuner with 14 radio station presets, a built-in clock/alarm with a 3-hour timer, Dolby B, auto-reverse, bass enhancer, remote-control wire and headphone. Player also includes a rechargeable battery charger and an AA battery adapter for regular batteries. Model RQ-S55V from Panasonic is $199.95.

Reprinted with permission from *Bottom Line Personal,* 330 W. 42nd St., New York, NY 10036. 24 issues per year/$49 per year or $4 per issue. (800) 274-5611.

194

INSPIRATIONAL WORDS ON DISK

The inspirational or amusing quotations that begin each major section of *201 Things to Do While You're Getting Better* are from a computer software program that may cheer you up immensely. Called Quotemaster Plus, it features 30,000 quotations on a variety of subjects, and it's available by mail for just $89. Additional Quotepacks contain 1,600 quotations on subjects like Humor, Motivational Ideas, Society, and Government/Politics (always good for a laugh!). For more information, call PennComp at (800) 326-6145 or write to: P.O. Box 271529, Houston, TX 77277-1529. A more extensive version of the program can also be ordered for $270. Quotemaster Plus is available for DOS, Macintosh, or Windows systems.

195
REMOTELY HELPFUL

A handy device that can save you from getting up when all you want to do is lie in bed is the Fox 800 Universal Remote Control. This centralized remote not only replaces up to eight other remotes, but also eliminates the confusing "which button does what" question common with other universal remotes. The eight buttons on this remote each relate to a specific device: TV, CD and laser disc players, VCR, stereo receiver, cable converters, tape player, and auxiliary unit. (If you wish, any button can substitute for an extra device.) Once a selection is pressed, the easy-to-read screen lists options that apply only to that particular device. Even recording a television program becomes a snap because all that's required is for you to enter the date, time, and channel. The remote turns on the VCR, changes the channel, and records the program. This model comes pre-programmed with the most popular infrared-controlled equipment and can learn from other remotes that are not pre-programmed. Backlit screen is great for use in the dark. 25-foot range. May be used with most cable boxes. Uses five AA batteries, which are included. $99.95 from Hammacher Schlemmer, (800) 543-3366. Or write the Hammacher Schlemmer Operations Center, 2515 E. 43rd St., P.O. Box 182256, Chattanooga, TN 37422.

196
SWEET DREAMS ARE MADE OF THIS

In a hospital (or even your home if it's in a noisy neighborhood), you know all too well how strange sounds can keep you from getting to sleep. Luckily, there's the Marsona Portable Sound Conditioner. This compact, solid-state device unobtrusively fills your rooms with a wide range of soothing nature sounds—from rain to waterfall. It's blissful sounds help level out both intermittent and constant noise. Comes with 6-foot power cord and travel case. $99 from Attitudes (800) 525-2468, 24 hours a day. Or write to: Attitudes, P.O. Box 61148, Sunnyvale, CA 94088-1148.

197
WEARABLE MASSAGE

Designed by a licensed massage therapist, the Vibralaxer™ wraparound collar closely duplicates the kneading movements of a masseur's fingers. Cordless and easy to use, it gives you a relaxing, hands-free neck and shoulder massage while you work, watch TV, read, or travel. The stimulating vibrations and pulsations reach three different muscle groups simultaneously, gently soothing tired and sore muscles. Runs on two AA batteries, which are not included in the price of $29 from Attitudes (800) 525-2468, 24 hours a day. Or write to: Attitudes, P.O. Box 61148, Sunnyvale, CA 94088-1148.

198
TRANSLATION PLEASE

If you find other languages intimidating, but you've always wanted to learn one, the World Mate pocket-sized data bank is the fun way to get started. This slim, streamlined pocket computer translates 10,500 words between English and many other languages including German, French, Spanish, Italian, Dutch, Portuguese, Polish, Swedish, Norwegian, Danish, Finnish, Russian, Japanese, and Chinese. Plus, this little marvel's 8K data bank holds your appointment calendar, address book, memos, shows the time in 128 cities, can be programmed to show the exchange rate between eight currencies, and more! It'll even play games with you to pass the time until visiting hours. World Mate also provides translations for 150 basic phrases in each language in 10 categories like Eating Out, Airport, and Hotel. It weighs only 8 ounces and is powered by four lithium batteries. $135 from Attitudes (800) 525-2468, 24 hours a day. Or write to: Attitudes, P.O. Box 61148, Sunnyvale, CA 94088-1148.

199
BONSAI BASICS

Bonsai, the art of growing miniature trees in a variety of containers, is an ancient Japanese form of relaxation, discipline, and beauty. Have a little patience, take a little time, and you'll be rewarded with a captivating bonsai tree. As you learn the special techniques involved in growing these miniatures, you'll begin to see the beauty again in small things. Inside a wooden box is a complete Bonsai Kit—including clay pots, seeds for one tree, growing material, professional leaf and root clippers, copper wire for training branches, and an instruction booklet to guide you in the ways of this age-old art form. It's suggested you start with a small seedling, if you can obtain one, and an extra pot is included for that purpose. $25 from Attitudes (800) 525-2468, 24 hours a day. Or write to: Attitudes, P.O. Box 61148, Sunnyvale, CA 94088-1148.

200
WORLDLY ENTERTAINMENT

At a lightweight 1 1/2 pounds, the Sangean Portable Band Radio is considered one of the best digital short-wave models available. International broadcasts are clearly received by the 13 short-wave bands while three other bands receive AM, FM, and long-wave stations. The digital tuner offers four options for selecting a station—keypad, scanning button, manual rotary dial, or one of the 45 programmable presets. Includes a built-in alarm clock, storage pouch, stereo headphones, and antenna. $269.95 from Hammacher Schlemmer, (800) 543-3366. Or write the Hammacher Schlemmer Operations Center, 2515 E. 43rd St., P.O. Box 182256, Chattanooga, TN 37422.

VCR PLUS = AN EVEN BIGGER PLUS

I'm not advocating spending all of your recuperative time watching TV, but it can be a great relaxer, especially late at night if you have trouble falling asleep. My favorite gadget for simplifying the operation of a VCR is the VCR Plus, since it means you no longer have to program your VCR to watch your favorite programs any hour of the day or night. (You do need a VCR that has wireless remote capability to take advantage of VCR Plus, however). Just enter the special "Plus Code" listed in TV Guide beside each program or in some local TV listings and the show will be recorded. To order a VCR Plus call (800) 258-4VCR.

AND FINALLY ...

Live for today; plan for tomorrow; do not grieve for yesterday.

—Edward J. Larschan

SOLUTIONS TO

PUZZLES GALORE

SOLUTION FOR PUZZLE 171
COUGH AND A COLD

C	A	P	S		E	L	S		S	I	N	E
A	L	A	I		R	A	H		E	G	O	N
D	O	C	T	O	R	D	E	N	T	O	N	S
S	T	E	I	N				I	T	T	O	
		N	E	W		I	L	L				
A	B	A		T	O	O	T		E	L	K	S
D	O	C	T	O	R	D	E	T	R	O	I	T
O	A	T	H		M	E	M	O		S	M	U
		E	S	S		S	T	E				
	L	E	A	N				A	N	D	E	S
D	O	C	T	O	R	K	I	L	D	A	R	E
A	C	H	E		O	I	L		E	R	I	E
D	O	O	R		T	D	K		R	E	N	D

HINT: Polygraph tests are useful, but their sometimes-ambivalent results are inadmissable as evidence. Haskell volunteered to take the test because he simply wanted Inspector Cross off his back. He knew the best way was to tell him the literal truth.

SOLUTION: Cross opened the telephone directory and saw a dog-eared page that might have been the one Haskell used to call for help. There was no doubt that he called a surgeon. Cross himself called the number – and heard the same story. That a tree surgeon didn't handle the problem Haskell described.

l

SOLUTION FOR PUZZLE 172
A SHOT IN THE ARM

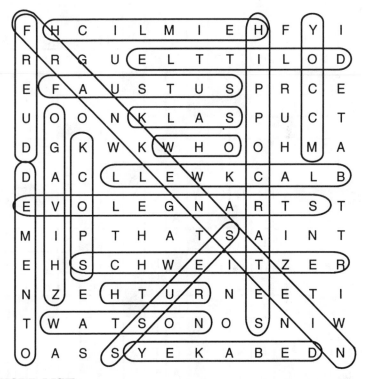

WORD LIST: BLACKWELL, DEBAKERY, DEMENTO, DOLITTLE, FAUSTUS, FRANKENSTEIN, FREUD, HEIMLICH, HIPPOCRATES, MCCOY, RUTH, SALK, SCHWEITZER, SUESS, SPOCK, STRANGELOVE, WATSON, WHO, ZHIVAGO

HINT: Doc had never seen the man before, so there was no personal grudge involved. And the gun wasn't loaded, so there was no actual danger to the customer. Inspector Cross is a fine judge of character, and he knew Doc's intentions were good. Now figure out what that intention was.

SOLUTION: Doc always liked to help people with health problems. When the man walked into the bar and asked for a glass of water, Doc tried to solve his problem by scaring him with a pistol in the face. It worked. The man walked out, thanking Doc for curing his hiccups.

SOLUTION FOR PUZZLE 173
PRESCRIPTION FOR MURDER

A	I	R	S		C	O	V	E		Z	O	O		R	I	G
T	R	I	O		E	V	I	L		A	R	M		B	A	A
✋	A	N	D	G	L	O	V	E		P	L	A	Y	I	N	G
		A	L	L		A	C	T		A	R	E				
N	U	R	S	E			T	O	O	N		W	I	F	E	
E	R	A		E	T	E	S		A	L	D	A		D	O	A
A	G	R	A		H	E	L	P		D	O	C	T	O	R	S
T	E	E	N		A	R	E	A	S		T	A	L	K	Y	
		🐟	B	R	O	W	P	E	N	C	I	L				
C	O	L	O	R			S	A	D	I	E		E	C	H	O
O	P	E	N	E	R	S		S	A	N	D		S	O	U	P
P	A	N		W	E	T	S		N	E	E	D		O	R	R
E	L	A	L		Q	U	I	Z			E	M	P	T	Y	
		E	A	U		P	E	T		A	M	I				
O	F	F	I	C	E	S		B	E	N	D	O	N	E	S	👂
A	L	A		E	S	P		R	E	A	D		I	G	O	T
T	U	X		S	T	Y		A	S	P	S		S	O	T	O

HINT: Mr. Felton was tired of playing nurse to his wife. But he didn't want suspicion to fall on him if she passed away. He thought of a foolproof scheme, but it required something found only in doctor's offices–preferably deceased ones.

SOLUTION: Mr. Felton was looking for prescription pads. He finally found one, and wrote his own prescription for a dangerous drug that would slowly poison Mrs. Felton. In case an autopsy revealed the cause, he could blame the doctor for the mistake, and the dead doctor would be unable to deny it.

SOLUTION FOR PUZZLE 174
INFECTIOUS CONDITION

SUBTITLE: The Doctor Diagnoses a Crime

SOLUTION: "The symptoms Dr. Porter found," said the Inspector, "were fever, congestion, and watery eyes. But it wasn't a bad cold. The doctor detected a highly contagious illness called rubeola–better known as measles. Unless those other two had immunity, look for bank robbers with a faceful of round red spots."

SOLUTION FOR PUZZLE 175
PAY THROUGH THE NOSE

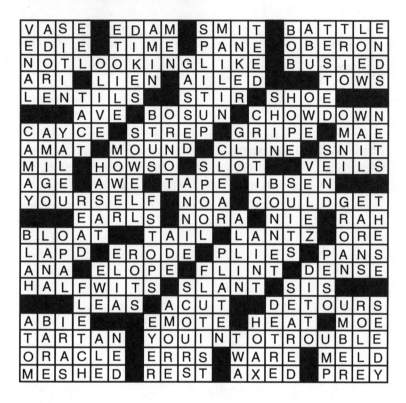

HINT: The doctor knew his stuff, and 'Big Nose' Burke's famous face was completely unrecognizable. But there are some circumstances when not looking like yourself can get you into trouble.

SOLUTION: 'Big Nose' Burke made his getaway in a hurry, and that was his downfall. Since Burke was leaving the country, he needed a passport–and even a faked passport couldn't have had a picture of his brand-new face. It was the Immigration office that put the cuffs on the robber.

INDEX

I Can Cope: Revised and Updated Second Edition by Judi Johnson and Linda Klein. Written in conjunction with the American Cancer Society's successful I CAN COPE program (which helps more than 50,000 people a year), the highly acclaimed *I Can Cope* is now completely revised and updated. *I Can Cope* is a landmark book that explores the feelings, problems, and obstacles that cancer patients face. With straightforward and valuable information and uplifting true stories of cancer survivors, the guide provides solid recommendations on how patients can gain control of their lives.
004236   ISBN 1-56561-039-3 $9.95   ☐

The Physician Within: Revised and Updated Second Edition by Catherine Feste. Through a positive approach, this acclaimed guide for those with chronic health conditions shows how to gain the motivation to establish healthy lifestyles..
004221   ISBN 1-56561-023-7 $10.95   ☐

Emergency Medical Treatment: Infants, Children, Adults Revised and Expanded Edition by Stephen Vogel, M.D., and David Manhoff, produced in cooperation with the National Safety Council. With over 1.5 million copies sold, the #1–selling guide of its kind has saved countless lives and is now totally updated with the newest safety guidelines. Written especially for people untrained in emergency medical procedures, this indispensable, step-by-step guide tells exactly what to do during the most common, life-threatening situations you might encounter for infants, children, and adults.
004627   ISBN 0-916363-10-4 $12.95   ☐

201 Things To Do While You're Getting Better (at Home or in the Hospital) by Erica Levy Klein is a unique self-help guide and activity-gift book rolled up in one. It's filled with important health information from the leading experts, amusing crossword puzzles, conundrums, and cartoons.
004230   ISBN 1-56561-033-4 $10.95   ☐

The Brand Name Pocket Guide to Additive-Free Foods by Michael J. Lapchick with Rosa A. Mo, R.D., Ed.D, is the first quick reference to over 1000 brand name products that are free from preservatives, artificial sweeteners, colors or flavors, and any other synthetic additives. You'll find most of the foods you already eat–complete with calorie, fat, cholesterol, sodium, carbohydrate, and exchange breakdowns.
004237   ISBN 1-56561-040-7 $9.95   ☐

How Should I Feed My Child? by Sandra K. Nissenberg, M.S., R.D., Margaret L. Bogle, Ph.D., R.D., Edna P. Langholz, M.S., R.D., and Audrey C. Wright, M.S., R.D. From four of the country's leading dietitians (who are mothers themselves), here's the definitive parenting guide on nutrition. Covering the prenatal months through the preschool years, this book provides parents-to-be and new parents clear and easy-to-use expert advice and the latest nutrition facts addressing real issues and parents' most common concerns.
004232   ISBN 1-56561-035-0 $12.95   ☐